Essential GCSE
Maths 4–5

Homework Book

Michael White

Elmwood Education

First published 2015 by
Elmwood Education Ltd
Unit 5, Mallow Park
Watchmead
Welwyn Garden City
AL7 1GX
Tel. 01707 333232

ISBN 9781 906 622 480

Typeset and illustrated by Tech-Set Ltd., Gateshead, Tyne and Wear.

CONTENTS

UNIT 7

Algebra 2

UNIT 8

Statistics 1

UNIT 9

Geometry 2

UNIT 10

Statistics 2

UNIT 11

Geometry 3

NUMBER 1   1

Do not use a calculator.

1 The product of two whole numbers is 91. Write down the two numbers.

2 Find the value of each calculation below, without using a calculator.

    a $\dfrac{16 - 4}{2 + 4}$ **b** $\dfrac{3^2 + 4^2}{10 - 5}$ **c** $\dfrac{(11 + 4) \times (18 - 13)}{5^2}$

    d $\sqrt{(5^2 + 12^2)}$ **e** $\dfrac{4 \times 4 + 4}{4 \times 10}$ **f** $\dfrac{6 + 9 \div 3}{(19 + 17) \div 4}$

3 36 people pay a total of £936 to visit the theatre. If each person pays the same amount, how much does each person pay?

4 250 football supporters from the same town travel to an away match. Four full coaches are used, costing £408 each. Each coach holds 54 people. The remaining people pay £17 each to travel by train.
If one extra coach had been used for the remaining people so they did not travel by train, how much money would each of the remaining people have saved?

5 Write down the answer to each of the following:

    a $0{\cdot}4 \times 0{\cdot}6$ **b** $0{\cdot}07 \times 0{\cdot}5$ **c** $6 - 1{\cdot}03$ **d** $20 \times 0{\cdot}06$

    e $0{\cdot}3^2$ **f** $1{\cdot}8 \times 15$ **g** $600 \times 0{\cdot}12$ **h** $17 - 2{\cdot}19$

6 Croissants are loaded into trays of 32. How many trays are used to deal with 1400 croissants?

7 A box of crisps contains 48 packets. Janine buys 263 boxes.
She pays 35p for each packet of crisps. She sells all the crisps at 60p per packet except for 150 packets which are damaged so cannot be sold.
How much profit does she make if she has additional overhead costs of £1641·12?

8 A glass holds 0·2 litre of squash. How many glasses can be filled from a 1·5 litre bottle of squash?

Use a calculator.

1 Each of the calculations below is wrong. Find the correct answer for each calculation.

    a $\dfrac{48 + 32}{20} = 49{\cdot}6$ **b** $\dfrac{51 - 31}{10} = 47{\cdot}9$ **c** $\dfrac{50}{25 \times 10} = 20$ **d** $\dfrac{75}{40 - 20} = -18{\cdot}125$

2 Work out the following, giving answers to the *nearest whole number.*
Match each calculation to the correct answer.

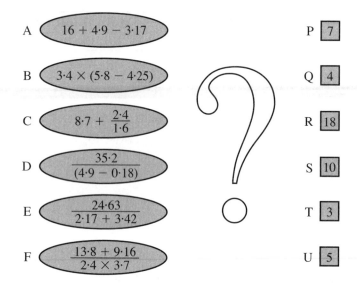

A $16 + 4\cdot9 - 3\cdot17$

B $3\cdot4 \times (5\cdot8 - 4\cdot25)$

C $8\cdot7 + \dfrac{2\cdot4}{1\cdot6}$

D $\dfrac{35\cdot2}{(4\cdot9 - 0\cdot18)}$

E $\dfrac{24\cdot63}{2\cdot17 + 3\cdot42}$

F $\dfrac{13\cdot8 + 9\cdot16}{2\cdot4 \times 3\cdot7}$

P $\boxed{7}$

Q $\boxed{4}$

R $\boxed{18}$

S $\boxed{10}$

T $\boxed{3}$

U $\boxed{5}$

3 A Bureau de Change offers $\$1\cdot568$ per £ but charges a commission fee of £3.
How many dollars (to the nearest cent) do you get for £75?

4 Which is larger?   A $\left(3\frac{2}{5}\right)^2$ or   B $20\frac{1}{4} \div 1\frac{7}{9}$

5 Write the numbers below in order of size, starting with the smallest.

$\boxed{3^4}$ $\boxed{2^7}$ $\boxed{5^3}$ $\boxed{1^9}$ $\boxed{4^4}$

6 Calculate the following, giving each answer to 3 significant figures.

a $\dfrac{17\cdot2 + 8\cdot16}{8\cdot61 - 2\cdot48}$

b $3\sqrt{8} - 5$

c $\dfrac{(-9\cdot1)^2 + 7\cdot13}{(-4\cdot28)^2}$

d $\dfrac{\sqrt{8} + \sqrt{2}}{\sqrt{7} - \sqrt{3}}$

e $\dfrac{-7\cdot3 + (-1\cdot9)^2}{(-1\cdot72) \times (-2\cdot4)}$

f $(\sqrt{6} - \sqrt{8})^4$

7 Arushi calculates that $0.5 \times \sqrt{141}$ is equal to 5.94, correct to 3 significant figures.
Explain clearly how Arushi can check her answer is probably correct *without using* a
calculator.

8 $\boxed{x} \xrightarrow{+} \boxed{2\frac{1}{4}} \xrightarrow{\times} \boxed{\frac{4}{5}} \xrightarrow{-} \boxed{1\frac{1}{3}} \xrightarrow{\div} \boxed{\frac{1}{2}} \xrightarrow{=} \boxed{4\frac{46}{75}}$

Work out the value of x.

9 The area of mould on a slice of bread is 1 cm² after 4 days. One day later the area has increased by one third of this size. It then increased by two-fifths of its new size by the end of day 6. It then increases by two-thirds of its new size by the end of day 7. Calculate the area of the mould after one week.

10 Estimate, correct to 1 significant figure:

a $\frac{9\cdot98 \times 30\cdot1}{0\cdot997}$ b $\frac{14\cdot9 + 4\cdot96^2}{17\cdot32 - 7\cdot4}$ c $\frac{11\cdot13^2 + 8\cdot9^2}{10\cdot2^2}$

TASK M1.3 **Main Book Page 6**

Remember: $a^m \times a^n = a^{m+n}$ $(a^m)^n = a^{mn}$
$a^m \div a^n = a^{m-n}$ $a^0 = 1$

1 Answer true or false for each statement below:

a $(5^4)^5 = 5^9$ b $3^4 \times 3^2 = 3^8$ c $7^3 \times 7 = 7^3$

d $\frac{2^6}{2} = 2^5$ e $\frac{(5^3)^3}{(5^2)^3} = 5^3$ f $\frac{(3^2)^4}{3} = 3^6$

2 Work out and write each answer as a number in index form.

a $6^5 \div 6^2$ b $(9^3)^4$ c $\frac{7^6}{7^3}$

d $\frac{5^6 \times 5^3}{5^2}$ e $\frac{2^8 \times 2^5}{2^4 \times 2^4}$ f $\frac{(8^2)^4 \times 8^4}{8^7}$

3 The area of the square opposite is 3^{10} mm². Write down the value of the side length x, giving the answer as a number in index form.

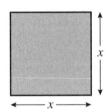

4 Copy and complete

a $\square \times 3^6 = 3^8$ b $7^4 \times \square = 7^9$ c $6^8 \div \square = 6^6$

d $\square \div 2^4 = 2^6$ e $\square \div 5^3 = 5^4$ f $\frac{3^6}{\square} = 3$

5 2^8 people live in a village. Five years later the population of the village has doubled. Write down the new population of the village, giving the answer as a number in index form.

6 Which is larger?

P $\boxed{\frac{(3^2)^5 \times 3^4}{3^7}}$ or Q $\boxed{\frac{3^4 \times 3^9}{3 \times (3^2)^2}}$

3

4

7 Evaluate (work out the value of)

    a $3^2 \times 2^3$ **b** $2^4 \times 5^3$ **c** $2^3 \times 3^3 \times 4^3$

8 Work out the area of the triangle opposite, giving the answer as a number in index form.

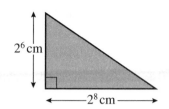

2^6 cm

2^8 cm

TASK E1.1   **Main Book Page 7**

1 3^{-2} (index form) $= \dfrac{1}{3^2} = \dfrac{1}{9}$ (ordinary number)

   Write the following as ordinary numbers:

   a 4^{-1} **b** 2^{-3} **c** 6^{-2} **d** 4^{-3}

   e 10^{-2} **f** 5^{-3} **g** 7^{-1} **h** 2^{-6}

> **Remember:**
>
> $a^{-n} = \dfrac{1}{a^n}$
>
> $\dfrac{1}{a^n}$ is the *reciprocal* of a^n

2 Write the following in negative index form:

   a $\dfrac{1}{4^2}$ **b** $\dfrac{1}{3^4}$ **c** $\dfrac{1}{2^5}$ **d** $\dfrac{1}{8^3}$

3 Write $\dfrac{1}{25}$ as a power of 5 in negative index form.

4 Write $\dfrac{1}{27}$ as a power of 3 in negative index form.

5 Answer true or false for each statement below:

   a $2^{-8} = \dfrac{1}{2^8}$ **b** $6^{-2} \times 6^{-2} = 6^{-4}$ **c** $9^{-1} = -9$

   d $3^{-5} = \dfrac{5}{3}$ **e** $\left(\dfrac{1}{4}\right)^{-1} = 4$ **f** $\left(\dfrac{2}{3}\right)^{-2} = \dfrac{9}{4}$

6 Work out the sum of the reciprocal of 4 and the reciprocal of 5.

7 Which is greater and by how much: the reciprocal or 3 or the reciprocal of 2?

8 Write the following as ordinary numbers:

   a $\left(\dfrac{1}{3}\right)^{-1}$ **b** $\left(\dfrac{3}{7}\right)^{-1}$ **c** $\left(\dfrac{3}{5}\right)^{-2}$ **d** $\left(\dfrac{2}{7}\right)^{-2}$

9 Express $\frac{1}{81}$ in the form 9^n.

10 Evaluate

    a $5^3 \times \frac{1}{25}$ **b** $\frac{1}{16} \times 2^9$ **c** $10^6 \times \frac{1}{1000} \times 10^{-2}$

11 Express $0{\cdot}1$ in the form 10^n

12 Is the reciprocal of a number x always smaller than the number x?
Explain your answer fully.

TASK M1.4	Main Book Page 9

> **Remember:** $\sqrt{7} \times \sqrt{7} = \sqrt{49} = 7$

Do not use a calculator.

1 Work out

    a $\sqrt{11} \times \sqrt{11}$ **b** $4 \times \sqrt{5} \times \sqrt{5}$ **c** $\frac{4\sqrt{9}}{\sqrt{16}}$

    d $\frac{3\sqrt{64} + \sqrt{36}}{7 + \sqrt{9}}$ **e** $(\sqrt{144} - \sqrt{81})^2$ **f** $(\sqrt{25} + \sqrt{9})(\sqrt{25} - \sqrt{9})$

2

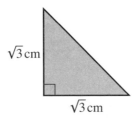

Work out the total area of the square and two triangles above.

3 Only one number in the list opposite is not
a *cube number*. Write down this number.

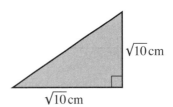

27   9
125
64   216   1

4 Evaluate

    a $\sqrt[3]{64}$ **b** $\sqrt[3]{(36 - 9)}$ **c** $\sqrt[3]{(7 \times 7 \times 7)}$ **d** $\sqrt[3]{(61 + 4^3)}$

5 Which gives the greater answer below and by how much:

    A $\boxed{\dfrac{\sqrt{36} \times \sqrt[3]{27}}{\sqrt{(48 + 33)}}}$ or   B $\boxed{\dfrac{\sqrt[3]{(64 \times 8)}}{\sqrt{16} - \sqrt[3]{8}}}$?

6 Use a calculator to work out the area of the shape opposite. All lengths are in cm.

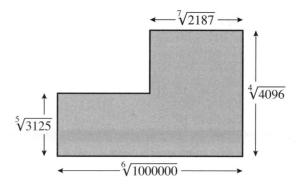

$\sqrt[7]{2187}$

$\sqrt[4]{4096}$

$\sqrt[5]{3125}$

$\sqrt[6]{1000000}$

7 Use a calculator to work out each of the following, leaving answers to 1 decimal place.

a $\sqrt[5]{(81 \times 3)}$

b $\dfrac{\sqrt[4]{1296} \times \sqrt[5]{32}}{\sqrt[6]{729}}$

c $\dfrac{\sqrt[6]{262144}}{\sqrt{(25^2 - 7^2)}}$

d $\sqrt[3]{\dfrac{5^3 + \sqrt{256}}{\sqrt[4]{2401}}}$

e $\dfrac{\sqrt[3]{15^2 - 4^3}}{\sqrt{7^3 - 17^2}}$

f $\sqrt{\dfrac{22^2 + 3^4}{\sqrt[5]{3125}}}$

10

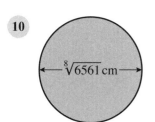

$\sqrt[8]{6561}$ cm

The diameter of a circle is shown opposite. Calculate the area of the circle, giving the answer to one decimal place.

TASK M1.5 ———————————————— **Main Book Page 10**

1 Match each number to the product of its factors. One answer is an odd one out.

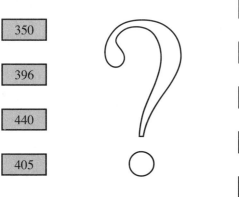

350

396

440

405

$2^3 \times 5 \times 11$

$2^2 \times 3 \times 7$

$2 \times 5^2 \times 7$

$3^4 \times 5$

$2^2 \times 3^2 \times 11$

2 Using any method, write the following numbers as products of prime factors, leaving each answer in index form:

a 96 **b** 150 **c** 310 **d** 520

3 Write all your answers to question **2** in index form if you have not already done so.

4 Write down the value of the square of the prime number which lies between 24 and 30.

5 Write down a cube number whose digits add up to 10.

6 Add up all the multiples of 35 which lie between the 11th largest square number and the 6th largest cube number.

| TASK M1.6 | Main Book Page 12 |

1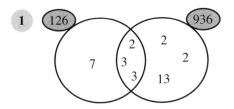

Use the Venn diagram to find
a the HCF of 126 and 936
b the LCM of 126 and 936

2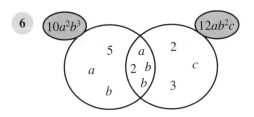

Use the Venn diagram to find
a the HCF of 700 and 60
b the LCM of 700 and 60

3 Draw factor trees and Venn diagrams to find the HCF and LCM of:
    a 420 and 308   **b** 875 and 2205   **c** 2079 and 4950

4 $4mn^2 = 2 \times 2 \times m \times n \times n$ $6m^3n^3 = 2 \times 3 \times m \times m \times m \times n \times n \times n$

    a Find the Highest Common Factor of $4mn^2$ and $6m^3n^3$.
    b Find the Lowest Common Multiple of $4mn^2$ and $6m^3n^3$.

5 The Highest Common Factor of two numbers is 8.
    The Lowest Common Multiple of the same two numbers is 48.
    Write down the two numbers.

6

Use this Venn diagram to find the Lowest Common Multiple of $10a^2b^3$ and $12ab^2c$.

7 Gill saves £105 each week for x weeks. Matt saves £147 each week for y weeks.
If Gill and Matt end up saving the same amount of money, write down the smallest possible values for x and y.

8 Lana buys some loaves of bread and some packs of ham slices. Each loaf of bread contains 22 slices and there are 8 ham slices in each pack. She makes ham sandwiches using 2 slices of bread and one ham slice in each sandwich. What is the least number of loaves and packs of ham Lana should buy if there is to be no bread or ham left over.

TASK M1.7 ——————————————————————————— **Main Book Page 13**

1 Write the numbers below in standard form.

a 47 000   b 7600   c 575   d 740 000

e 369 000   f 0·0032   g 0·089   h 0·864

> **Remember:**
>
> a standard form number will have the form $A \times 10^n$ where $1 \leqslant A < 10$

2 $38\,000 = 38 \times 10^3$. This number is not written in standard form.
Write it correctly in standard form.

3 Write each number below as an ordinary number.

a 5×10^5 b 6×10^3 c 4×10^{-2} d $1\cdot8 \times 10^4$

e $8\cdot3 \times 10^5$ f $5\cdot7 \times 10^{-3}$ g $2\cdot38 \times 10^3$ h $4\cdot29 \times 10^{-1}$

4 Which number below is larger:

| $2\cdot9 \times 10^4$ | or | $3\cdot18 \times 10^3$ | ?

5 Write the numbers below in order, starting with the smallest.

| $7\cdot4 \times 10^{-3}$ | | $7\cdot68 \times 10^{-4}$ | | $7\cdot42 \times 10^{-3}$ | ?

6 Write the numbers below in standard form.

a 0·03   b 308   c 5 million   d 0·0004

e 228·7   f 200 million   g 46·73   h 0·092

i 78 000 000   j 0·96   k three hundredths   l 620 000

7 Jack earns £32 600 each year. Lucy earns £($3\cdot19 \times 10^5$) each year.
How much more money does Lucy earn than Jack?

TASK M1.8 ————————————————————————

Do not use a calculator.

1 Write each number below in standard form.

    a 73×10^4 **b** 42×10^{14} **c** 0.8×10^7 **d** 0.32×10^{24}

    e 0.68×10^{-4} **f** 374×10^{-7} **g** 425×10^{38} **h** 0.56×10^{-7}

2 Find the area of this rectangle, leaving your answer in standard form.

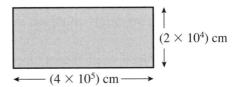

(2×10^4) cm

$\longleftarrow (4 \times 10^5) \text{ cm} \longrightarrow$

3 Work out the following, leaving each answer in standard form.

    a $(2 \times 10^8) \times (2.5 \times 10^7)$ **b** $(1.5 \times 10^6) \times (4 \times 10^3)$

    c $(3.5 \times 10^9) \times (2 \times 10^{-4})$ **d** $(1.7 \times 10^{-18}) \times (4 \times 10^{-8})$

    e $(4 \times 10^{12}) \times (3 \times 10^7)$ **f** $(9 \times 10^{17}) \times (4 \times 10^{28})$

    g $(8 \times 10^{21}) \div (4 \times 10^6)$ **h** $(7 \times 10^{19}) \div (2 \times 10^7)$

    i $\dfrac{9 \times 10^{32}}{4.5 \times 10^{-5}}$ **j** $(4 \times 10^5)^2$

    k $(8.7 \times 10^{12}) \div (3 \times 10^{-16})$ **l** $\dfrac{3 \times 10^{48}}{6 \times 10^{13}}$

4 Calli has £(4×10^5) and Carl has £(3×10^4). They put their money together.
    Write down the total amount of money they have, giving your answer in standard form.

5 Work out the following, leaving each answer in standard form.

    a $(5 \times 10^6) + (7 \times 10^5)$ **b** $(9 \times 10^8) - (4 \times 10^7)$ **c** $(4.8 \times 10^{12}) - (1.9 \times 10^{11})$

    d $(3 \times 10^{-2}) - (9 \times 10^{-3})$ **e** $(4.3 \times 10^{-8}) + (2 \times 10^{-7})$ **f** $(6.4 \times 10^{24}) + (5.6 \times 10^{23})$

6

Work out the volume of this triangular prism. Give the answer in standard form.

6×10^8 cm

5×10^{10} cm

4×10^7 cm

7 What number must be added to 3600 to give the answer 4.5×10^4?
    Give the answer in standard form.

8 In a TV popstar show final, the number of votes for each contestant is shown below:

Gary Tallow $(9 \cdot 6 \times 10^5)$ votes
Nina X $(1 \cdot 3 \times 10^6)$ votes
Rosa Williams $(1 \cdot 85 \times 10^6)$ votes

a Who got the most votes?
b How many people voted in total?

9 Work out $(7 \times 10^{-12})^3$, leaving your answer in standard form.

10 The population of Hatton is one hundred times greater than the population of Tarly.
Write down the population of Hatton in standard form if the population of Tarly is $3 \cdot 62 \times 10^3$.

TASK M1.9	Main Book Page 17

Use a calculator.

1 Last year a company made a profit of £$(6 \cdot 18 \times 10^6)$. This year it made a profit of £$(1 \cdot 9 \times 10^7)$.
Work out the total profit for both years, giving the answer in standard form.

2 Work out the following, leaving each answer in standard form correct to 3 significant figures.

a $\dfrac{(5 \cdot 6 \times 10^{21}) \times (2 \cdot 7 \times 10^{28})}{5 \times 10^{13}}$

b $\dfrac{(7 \cdot 4 \times 10^{-13}) \times (3 \cdot 94 \times 10^{-26})}{4 \cdot 2 \times 10^{18}}$

c $\dfrac{(3 \cdot 8 \times 10^{23}) - (9 \cdot 7 \times 10^{22})}{1 \cdot 8 \times 10^{-17}}$

d $\dfrac{(4 \cdot 89 \times 10^{16})^2}{2 \cdot 14 \times 10^9}$

e $\sqrt{\dfrac{(4 \cdot 83 \times 10^{14}) + (3 \cdot 16 \times 10^{15})}{2 \cdot 82 \times 10^{-12}}}$

f $\dfrac{\sqrt{5 \cdot 28 \times 10^{31}}}{(4 \cdot 9 \times 10^{-10}) + (2 \cdot 7 \times 10^{-9})}$

g $\dfrac{(7 \cdot 3 \times 10^{14})^2}{(3 \cdot 92 \times 10^{-15}) \times (2 \cdot 8 \times 10^{-23})}$

h $\sqrt{\dfrac{(3 \cdot 48 \times 10^{15}) \times (2 \cdot 19 \times 10^{26})}{(4 \cdot 37 \times 10^{12}) + (1 \cdot 95 \times 10^{11})}}$

3 In 2010 the population of a country was $9 \cdot 2 \times 10^9$. Over the next five years the population rose by 15%. Find the population in 2015.

4 The diameter of the earth is $1 \cdot 3 \times 10^7$ m. Assuming that the earth is a perfect sphere, find the circumference of the earth. Give your answer in standard form to 2 significant figures.

5 $E = mgh$. Find the value of h to 3 significant figures in standard form if $E = 3 \cdot 78 \times 10^4$, $m = 2 \cdot 3 \times 10^2$ and $g = 9 \cdot 81$.

6 The values of 6 properties are shown in the table below.

	Value (£'s)
A	$1{\cdot}7 \times 10^5$
B	$4{\cdot}5 \times 10^5$
C	$1{\cdot}28 \times 10^6$
D	$5{\cdot}1 \times 10^5$
E	$9{\cdot}5 \times 10^4$
F	$2{\cdot}25 \times 10^5$

a Which property is half the value of property B?

b Which property is treble the value of property A?

c Write the properties out in order of value, starting with the lowest.

d Find the total value of all 6 properties, giving the answer in standard form.

7 The population of a certain country is $5{\cdot}7 \times 10^8$ and its area is $7{\cdot}21 \times 10^{10}\,\text{m}^2$. Find the population density (people per m²) of this country. Give your answer in standard form to 2 significant figures.

8 The population of a certain type of bird increased from $7{\cdot}8 \times 10^3$ to $1{\cdot}2 \times 10^4$ over a ten year period. Find the percentage increase over that period, giving your answer to 3 significant figures.

9 The speed of light is approximately $2{\cdot}8 \times 10^8\,\text{m/s}$. Express this in km/h in standard form to 3 significant figures.

ALGEBRA 1   2

TASK M2.1 ———————————————————————— **Main Book Page 26**

Simplify:

1 $6m \times 3n$

2 $35n \div 5$

3 $4a \times 3a$

4 $\dfrac{m^2}{m}$

5 $\dfrac{a^3}{a}$

6 $9 \times 3n \times 2m$

7 Jake says that:

$$3a + 4ab + 2b = 9a^2b^2$$

Sally says that Jake is incorrect. Explain fully why Sally thinks that Jake has made a mistake.

8 P $\;5(a + 3) = 5a + 15\;$ or Q $\;5(a + 3) = 5a + 3$

Which answer above is correct and describe the mistake that has been made in the other answer.

9 Expand:

   a $4(m + 7)$ **b** $5(3a + 5)$ **c** $2(n - 7m)$ **d** $n(n - 3m)$

   e $m(2m + 9)$ **f** $3a(2a - 1)$ **g** $5m(m - 2n)$ **h** $6a(2a + 5b)$

10 Collect like terms:

   a $6m + 3n - 2m + 8n$ **b** $4n + 2m + 1 - n$ **c** $5n + 6m - 3m + 2n^2$

11 Write down an expression for the perimeter of the isosceles triangle opposite. Simplify the expression.

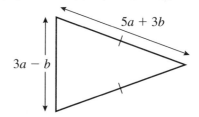

12

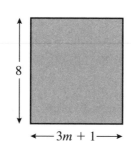

Write down and simplify an expression for the sum of the areas of the two rectangles shown opposite.

TASK M2.2 ———————————————————————— **Main Book Page 27**

Solve these equations:

1 $7n - 9 = 40$ **2** $\dfrac{n}{8} = 9$ **3** $35 = 4n + 3$

4 $\dfrac{n}{6} = 7$ **5** $14 = 3n - 1$ **6** $9n - 17 = 19$

7 Stella needs to factorise $21m + 35n$. She takes out the common factor 7 and writes $7(3m + 5n)$. Explain clearly what she needs to do in order to check if her answer is correct.

Factorise:

8 $18a - 27b$ **9** $12m + 16n$ **10** $m^2 + 3m$

11 $a^2 - 7ab$ **12** $2xy - x^2$ **13** $8n^2 + 6mn$

14 5^7 is a number written in *index form*.
Work out the area of the rectangle opposite, giving the answer in index form.

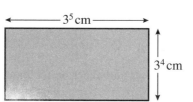

15

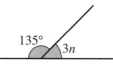

135° 3n

a Write down an equation for the diagram opposite.

b Solve the equation to find the value of n.

16

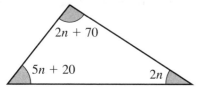

$2n + 70$

$5n + 20$ $2n$

a Write down an equation for the diagram opposite.

b Solve the equation to find the value of n.

Write each answer below in index form.

17 $5^2 \times 5 \times 5^3$

18 $6^7 \div 6^4$

19 $\dfrac{2^6 \times 2^2}{2^5}$

20 $\dfrac{7^3 \times 7^5}{7^2 \times 7^2}$

21 $\dfrac{3^{10}}{3^4 \times 3^3}$

22 $\dfrac{8^2 \times 8^4 \times 8^2}{8 \times 8^3 \times 8}$

23 Write down and simplify an expression for the sum of the areas of the two rectangles shown opposite.

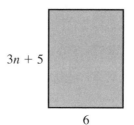

$3n + 5$

6

4

$4n + 3$

24 Expand and simplify:

$6(2x + 7) + 5x + 3(7x + 2)$

25 Pat says that $3m \times 6n \times 4p$ is the same as $6p \times 2m \times 6n$. Max does not agree. Who is correct? Explain your answer clearly.

| **TASK E2.1** | **Main Book Page 28** |

1 AD is twice as long as the side BC. Write down and simplify the expression for the perimeter of shape ABCD opposite.

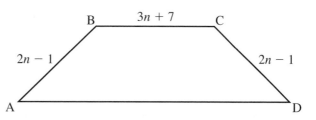

B $3n + 7$ C

$2n - 1$ $2n - 1$

A   D

2 Simplify the expressions below.

a $\dfrac{m^8 \times m^3}{m^2 \times m^4}$

b $\dfrac{(n^5)^3 \times n^4}{n^9}$

c $7n^6 \times 4n^3$

d $\dfrac{48m^7}{4m^4}$

e $\dfrac{(n^2)^4 \times (n^3)^2}{n^5 \times (n^3)^2}$

f $\dfrac{8m^5 \times 5m^4}{10m^7}$

3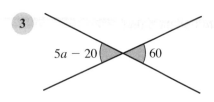

a Write down an equation for the diagram opposite.

b Solve the equation to find the value of a.

4 Write down whether each statement below is true or false:

a $-5m \times -3m = -15m^2$

b $-6n + 4n = -24n^2$

c $(-4n)^2 = 16n^2$

d $-24m \div -6 = 4m$

e $10a^2 \div -5a = -2a^2$

f $-9m \times 6n = -54mn$

5 Nevin says that $15xy - 10x^2 = 5x(3y - 2x)$.
Show clearly if Nevin is correct or not.

6 Solve these equations.

a $3n + 4 = 3$

b $7n + 6 = 4$

c $7 = 3n + 19$

d $4n + 17 = 9$

e $23 - 4n = 7$

f $6 = 2n + 7$

7 The length AG is double BE and the length FG is double DE. Write down and simplify an expression for the area of shape ABCDEFG.

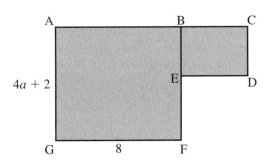

8 Tamzin must factorise $16a^2 - 8ab$.
There are five possible answers below.

$8a(2a - b)$	$a(16a - 8b)$	$4a(4a - 2b)$	$6a(10a - 2b)$	$2a(8a - 4b)$
P	Q	R	S	T

Which is the only answer which is *not* correct?

9 Factorise completely:

a $4n^2 - 10mn$

b $30pq - 15p^2$

c $16m^2 + 12m$

d $36x^2 + 20xy$

e $10m + 5mn + 20m^2$

f $56xy - 40y^2$

10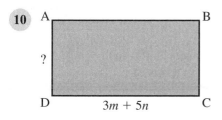

The area of the rectangle opposite is $18mn + 30n^2$.
Write down an expression for the width AD.

TASK E2.2 ──────────────────────────── **Main Book Page 30**

Expand and simplify:

1 $3(a + 4) + 7$

2 $9(2b + 4) + 4b$

3 $7(5a + 6) - 10a$

Simplify

4 $3(8y + 6) + 2(2y - 5)$

5 $5n + 9 + 6(2n + 3)$

6 $4b + 9(3b + 6) - 24$

7 $7(4c + 7) + 3(2c - 8)$

8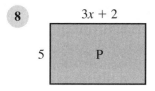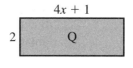

Six rectangles with the dimensions of rectangle P are joined to 5 rectangles with the dimensions of rectangle Q. Write down and simplify an expression for the total area of the combined rectangles.

Copy and complete:

9 $6(3a + 2) - 4(2a + 2) = \boxed{} + 12 - \boxed{} - 8 = \boxed{} + 4$

10 $7(4x + 3) - 5(3x - 6) = 28x + \boxed{} - 15x + \boxed{} = 13x + \boxed{}$

Expand and simplify:

11 $5(a + 4) - 3(a + 2)$

12 $6(2m + 3) - 5(m + 3)$

13 $4(5y + 6) - 2(4y + 3)$

14 $2(8b + 9) - 4(4b - 6)$

15 $8a - 3(2a - 5) + 6$

16 $7x - 4(x - 1) - 3$

17 $9(4n + 7) - 5(2n + 4)$

18 $10q + 3(5 - 2q) + 4(7q + 4)$

19 $3x(2x + 3) + 5x(x - 2)$

20 $5n(3n^2 - 4) - 2n(4n^2 + 5)$

21 $4m(2m - n) - 3n(4m + n)$

22 $3a(4a + 2b - 3c) - 4b(5a - 2c)$

TASK M2.3 ───────────────────────── **Main Book Page 31**

1 Alyssa buys x pints of milk at 62p each. She also buys $(x + 1)$ eggs at 48p each.
Write down a formula for the total cost c of the milk and eggs, in terms of x.

2
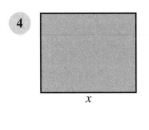

Write down a formula for the perimeter P
of the isosceles triangle in terms of x.

3 Anton sells cakes at £2 each. Each day it costs him £15 to make the cakes.
One day he sells m cakes. Write down a formula for the amount £A of profit he
makes from selling these cakes.

4
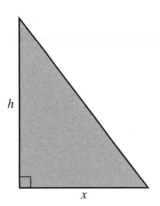

The height h of the triangle
opposite is double the base.
Write down a formula for the
area A of the triangle added to
the area of the square. Give the
answer in terms of x.

5 A factory makes shirts and jackets. Each shirt has n buttons and each jacket has $(n + 2)$ buttons.
A shop buys 80 shirts and 40 jackets. Write down a formula for the total number of buttons, T,
in terms of n for these shirts and jackets.

6 A car can be hired for £45 per day plus £0·25 per mile.
Write down a formula for the total cost C of hiring a car for x days and driving it for y miles.
Give your answer in terms of x and y.

7 During the morning a factory makes n pencils each hour. In the afternoon the factory makes
$(n - 40)$ pencils each hour. How many pencils, P, are made on one day if the factory is
running for 4 hours in the morning and 5 hours in the afternoon?

8 The lengths of the sides of the
parallelogram ABCD are such
that $AD : AB = 3 : 1$
Write down a formula for
the perimeter P in terms of n.

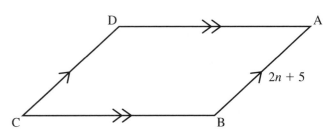

9 Ava has £n. Olivia has four times as much money as Ava. Dylan has £20 more than Olivia.

    a Write down an expression, in terms of n, for how much more money Dylan has than Ava.

    b Olivia spends half her money. Write down a formula for £T, the total amount of money all three people now have.

10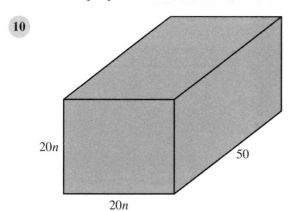

All lengths opposite are in cm.
Each side of the square cross-sectional area is decreased by 20%.
The length 50 cm is increased by 30%.
Write down an expression, in terms of n, for the volume, V, of the cuboid after the changes.

TASK M2.4/E2.3   **Main Book Page 33**

1 The total surface area A of this cuboid is given by the formula

$$A = 2lw + 2lh + 2hw$$

Find the value of A when

    a $l = 5$, $w = 3$ and $h = 1$

    b $l = 10$, $w = 2{\cdot}5$ and $h = 4$

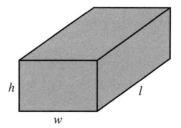

2 The total surface area A of a sphere is given by the formula

$$A = 12r^2$$

Find the value of A when

    a $r = 3$ **b** $r = 5$ **c** $r = 8$

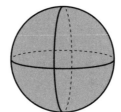

3 Energy E is given by the formula $E = mc^2$ where m is the mass and c is the speed of light. Find the value of E when $m = 15$ and $c = 300\,000\,000$.

4 Find the value of y using formulas and values given below:

    a $y = 4x + c$ when $x = 17$ and $c = -3$

    b $y = x^2 - b$ when $x = -3$ and $b = 2$

    c $y = \dfrac{x}{9} + \dfrac{z}{4}$ when $x = 54$ and $z = 68$

    d $y = x^2 + 8x$ when $x = -10$

5 The formula $s = ut + \dfrac{1}{2}at^2$ gives the displacement s of a particle after time t.

The acceleration is a and the initial velocity is u.

Find s (to 3 significant figures if necessary) when

a $u = 3, t = 12$ and $a = 6{\cdot}4$ **b** $u = -8{\cdot}17, a = -9{\cdot}81, t = 4{\cdot}5$

6 The area A of a trapezium is given by the formula

$$A = \frac{1}{2}h(a + b)$$

Find the value of A when

a $a = 6, b = 13, h = 12$ **b** $h = 3{\cdot}26, a = 4{\cdot}9, b = 7{\cdot}48$

7 The length of the diagonal AB is given by the formula

$$AB = \sqrt{(x^2 + y^2 + z^2)}$$

Find the value of AB when $x = 13$ cm, $y = 8$ cm and $z = 5$ cm.

(Give your answer to one decimal place.)

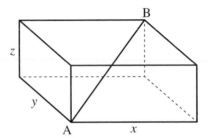

8 The mass m of a radioactive substance present at time t is given by the formula

$$m = 100(2^{-t})$$

Find the value of m when

a $t = 0$ **b** $t = 1$ **c** $t = 4$

TASK M2.5   **Main Book Page 36**

1 Copy and complete the following:

a $(x + 2)\,(x + 5)$

$= x^2 + 5x + \boxed{} + 10$

$= x^2 + \boxed{} + 10$

b $(x + 7)\,(x + 3)$

$= x^2 + \boxed{} + 7x + \boxed{}$

$= x^2 + \boxed{} + \boxed{}$

c $(x + 8)\,(x + 2)$

$= \boxed{} + \boxed{} + 8x + 16$

$= \boxed{} + \boxed{} + 16$

Multiply out the following:

2 $(x + 4)\,(x + 6)$ **3** $(m + 7)\,(m + 5)$ **4** $(y + 10)\,(y + 4)$

5 $(n + 6)\,(n + 7)$ **6** $(a + 2)\,(a + 9)$ **7** $(x + 12)\,(x + 3)$

8 Work out the area of this square, giving your answer in terms of x.

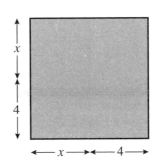

Expand:

9 $(x + 6)(x + 6)$

10 $(x + 7)^2$

11 $(x + 1)^2$

12 $(x + 9)^2$

13 $(y + 10)^2$

14 $(m + 5)^2$

TASK E2.4 ——————————————————— **Main Book Page 37**

1 Copy and complete the following:

a $(x + 3)(x - 5)$

$= x^2 - \boxed{} + 3x - 15$

$= x^2 - \boxed{} - 15$

b $(y - 4)(y - 4)$

$= y^2 - \boxed{} - 4y + \boxed{}$

$= y^2 - \boxed{} + \boxed{}$

c $(n - 8)(n + 5)$

$= \boxed{} + 5n - \boxed{} - 40$

$= \boxed{} - \boxed{} - 40$

Expand:

2 $(x + 4)(x - 6)$

3 $(a - 6)(a - 5)$

4 $(y - 3)(y - 7)$

5 $(n - 9)(n + 4)$

6 $(m + 7)(m - 6)$

7 $(b + 5)(b - 8)$

8 $(a - 8)(a - 8)$

9 $(x - 3)(x - 4)$

10 $(f + 10)(f - 7)$

Multiply out the following:

11 $(n - 5)(n - 5)$

12 $(y - 7)^2$

13 $(a - 2)^2$

14 $(4 + x)(x + 7)$

15 $(p - 3)^2$

16 $(m + 2)(8 - m)$

17 Louis says that the area of each shape shown opposite is equal. Show clearly whether he is correct or not.

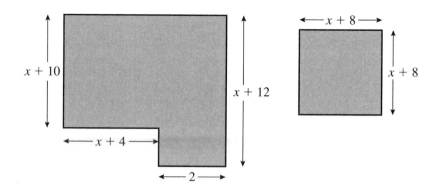

Expand:

18 $(3x + 2)(5x + 4)$

19 $(5a + 4)(2a + 1)$

20 $(2n - 4)(3n + 7)$

21 $(7y - 6)(3y - 2)$

22 $(4a + 6)^2$

23 $(5m - 9)^2$

24 $(6 + 5y)(6 + y)$

25 $(9 - 4c)(7 + 2c)$

26 $(4x - 2y)(8x + 3y)$

27 Expand and simplify $(m + 4)^2 + (m + 7)^2$

TASK M2.6 ———————————————————————————— **Main Book Page 39**

1 How many terms does the expression $3x^2 - 4x$ have?

2 $6n + 4 = 3n + 16$
Dave says that this is an equation because it is only true for one value of n.
Beth says it is an identity because it is true for all values of n. Show clearly who is correct.

3 Expand $(a + b)(a - b)$.
How many terms does the final simplified expression contain?

4 Show that
$$(x + 9)(x - 3) \equiv x^2 + 6x - 27$$
For how many different values of x is this true?

5

A $\boxed{x^3 + 8x}$

B $\boxed{5x - 2 = 8}$

C $\boxed{6x^2}$

D $\boxed{3x - 1 \geqslant 8}$

Which boxes here only contain:

a equations
b inequalities
c expressions
d identities
e one term?

E $\boxed{9x - 2 = 1 - 3x}$

F $\boxed{x(x - 3) \equiv x^2 - 3x}$

G $\boxed{5x^2 - 3x + 2}$

H $\boxed{(x + 1)^2 \equiv x^2 + 2x + 1}$

6 Prove whether each identity is correct or not.

    a $(x + 5)(x - 2) \equiv x^2 + 3x - 10$ **b** $2x(3x - 4) \equiv 5x^2 - 6x$

    c $(x - 3)(x - 3) \equiv x^2 - 6x + 9$ **d** $(4x + 5)^2 \equiv 16x^2 + 40x + 25$

7 Sometimes an '=' sign is used in place of an '≡' sign. For each part below, write down whether it is an equation or an identity. Explain your reasons fully.

    a $(x + 6)(x + 3) = x^2 + 9x + 18$ **b** $(x - 7)^2 = x^2 - 14x + 49$

    c $2(3x - 1) = 4x + 10$ **d** $8y^2(y + 3) = 8y^3 + 24y^2$

8 $x^2(5x^2 - 2x + 7) = 5x^4 - 2x^3 + 7x^2$
    For how many different values of x is this true?
    Is this an equation or an identity?

TASK M2.7 ——————————————————————————— **Main Book Page 41**

In questions **1** to **3** , copy and fill the empty boxes.

1 $4(n + 2) = 20$ **2** $3(2n + 3) = 15$ **3** $2(2n - 3) = 14$

    $4n + \boxed{8} = 20$ $6n + \boxed{} = 15$ $\boxed{} - 6 = 14$

        $4n = \boxed{}$ $6n = \boxed{}$ $\boxed{} = 20$

         $n = \boxed{}$ $n = \boxed{}$ $n = \boxed{}$

Solve these equations:

4 $3(n + 1) = 15$ **5** $5(n + 4) = 30$ **6** $10(n - 4) = 70$

7 $4(n - 3) = 24$ **8** $6(x - 5) = 18$ **9** $2(2x + 3) = 14$

10 $5(2x - 1) = 25$ **11** $3(2n + 7) = 27$ **12** $6(n - 4) = 36$

13 I think of a number. I add 9 onto the number then multiply the answer by 3.
     This gives 36. What was the number I started with?

Solve:

14 $12 = 2(2x - 4)$ **15** $52 = 4(2n + 5)$ **16** $2(3n - 5) = 20$

17 $54 = 3(3x + 6)$ **18** $5(2n - 6) = 40$ **19** $20 = 4(2x - 7)$

TASK E2.5 ——————————————————————————— **Main Book Page 42**

In questions **1** to **3** , copy and fill the empty boxes.

1 $2(n + 5) = 11$

$\boxed{} + 10 = 11$

$\boxed{} = 1$

$n = \dfrac{\boxed{}}{\boxed{}}$

2 $3(2n + 3) = 3$

$6n + \boxed{} = 3$

$6n = \boxed{}$

$n = \boxed{}$

3 $5(x + 2) = 8$

$5x + \boxed{} = 8$

$5x = \boxed{}$

$x = \dfrac{\boxed{}}{\boxed{}}$

Solve these equations:

4 $2(n + 3) = 3$

5 $5(x + 2) = 6$

6 $3(2x - 1) = 2$

7 $5(2x + 3) = 18$

8 $4(n - 2) = 11$

9 $6 = 3(n + 4)$

10 $18 = 2(6 - x)$

11 $70 = 10(2 - 5x)$

12 $3(2n + 5) = 14$

TASK M2.8 ——————————————————————————— **Main Book Page 43**

Find the value of n in questions **1** to **4** :

1

2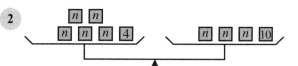

3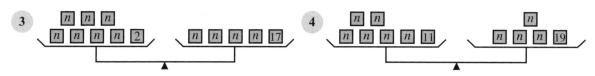

4

Solve these equations:

5 $5n + 9 = 4n + 18$

6 $8n + 7 = 3n + 2$

7 $7x + 6 = 3x + 18$

8 $9x + 1 = 2x + 43$

In questions **9** and **10** , copy and fill the empty boxes.

9 $6n - 3 = 2n + 17$

$4n - 3 = 17$

$4n = 20$

$n = \boxed{}$

10 $8x - 9 = 3x + 26$

$\boxed{} - 9 = 26$

$\boxed{} = 35$

$x = \boxed{}$

Solve these equations:

11 $5n - 3 = 2n + 18$

12 $8n - 3 = 2n + 27$

13 $4n - 9 = 3n + 7$

14 $9x - 6 = 6x + 18$

15 $6x + 12 = 2x + 20$

16 $8x - 10 = 5x + 20$

17 $5x - 7 = x + 29$

18 $4n + 13 = 2n + 25$

19 $7n - 8 = 3n + 28$

20 $10x - 6 = 7x + 15$

| TASK E2.6 | Main Book Page 44 |

In questions **1** to **3** , copy and fill the empty boxes.

1 $5x + 12 = 2x + 10$
$3x + 12 = 10$
$3x = \boxed{}$
$x = \dfrac{\boxed{}}{\boxed{}}$

2 $3(2x + 4) = 4(x + 6)$
$6x + \boxed{} = \boxed{} + 24$
$2x = \boxed{}$
$x = \boxed{}$

3 $5n + 2 = 3n - 8$
$2n + 2 = -8$
$2n = \boxed{}$
$n = \dfrac{\boxed{}}{\boxed{}}$

Solve these equations:

4 $4x + 3 = x + 4$

5 $7n + 4 = 2n + 8$

6 $5n + 3 = 27 - n$

7 $3x + 9 = 44 - 2x$

8 $6x + 10 = 4x + 6$

9 $5x + 19 = 11 - 3x$

10 This is an *isosceles* triangle.
Find the value of x.

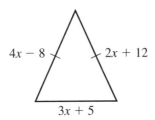

$4x - 8$ $2x + 12$

$3x + 5$

Solve:

11 $4(2x + 1) = 2(3x + 5)$

12 $5(3x + 4) = 4(3x + 20)$

13 $2(4x - 3) = 5(x + 6)$

14 $4(3n - 1) = 2(5n + 7)$

15 $5(2n + 4) = 2(4n + 3)$

16 $3(3x + 2) + 5(x + 4) = 54$

17 $5(2x + 3) + 2 = 2(3x + 4) + 21$

18 $4(6x + 1) + 22 = 5(4x - 3) - 3$

1 **a** Write down an equation using the angles.

   b Find x.

   c Write down the actual value of each angle in this triangle.

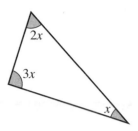

2 The area of this rectangle is $60\,\text{cm}^2$.

   a Write down an equation involving x.

   b Find x.

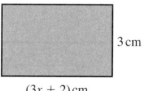

$3\,\text{cm}$

$(3x + 2)\,\text{cm}$

3 Colin has four times more sweets than Aubrey. Layla has 6 sweets less than Aubrey. Layla now eats two of her sweets. They all now have a total of 40 sweets. How many sweets does Aubrey have? (Hint: let x = number of Aubrey's sweets.)

4 The perimeter of the rectangle opposite is $50\,\text{cm}$.

   a Write down an equation using the perimeter.

   b Find x.

   c Write down the actual length and width of the rectangle.

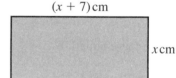

$(x + 7)\,\text{cm}$

$x\,\text{cm}$

5 Hannah has 3 times as much money as Joe. Hannah spends £24 on a new blouse. She now has £30 left. How much money has Joe got?

6 The length of a rectangle is $8\,\text{cm}$ more than its width. If its perimeter is $44\,\text{cm}$, find its width.

7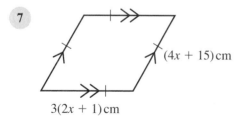

$(4x + 15)\,\text{cm}$

$3(2x + 1)\,\text{cm}$

A rhombus is shown opposite. Find the value of x.

8 Rishi is $1\,\text{cm}$ taller than Maria. Maria is $1\,\text{cm}$ taller than Emma. The sum of their heights is $480\,\text{cm}$. How tall is Emma?

1

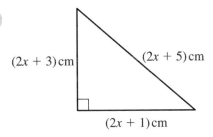

(2x + 3) cm   (2x + 5) cm

(2x + 1) cm

The perimeter of the triangle opposite is 24 cm.
Work out the actual area of the triangle.

2 **a** Write down an equation using the angles
 b Find x.
 c Write down the actual value of each angle in this quadrilateral.

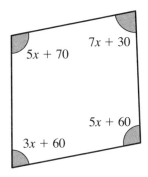

5x + 70   7x + 30

3x + 60   5x + 60

3 Three consecutive whole numbers add up to 144. If the lowest number is n,
 a write down an expression for the other two numbers in terms of n.
 b write down an equation involving n.
 c find n then write down the three consecutive whole numbers.

4 The area of each rectangle is equal (all lengths are measured in cm).
 a Find the value of x.
 b Find the area of one of the rectangles.

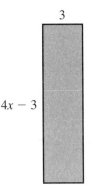

3

4x − 3

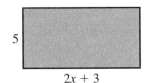

5

2x + 3

5 Evelyn writes down four consecutive whole numbers. The first, second and fourth numbers add up to 36 more than the value of the third number. Write down the actual 4 numbers.

6 This is an *isosceles* triangle.
 a Find the value of x.
 b Find the perimeter of the triangle.

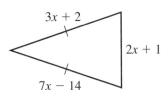

3x + 2

2x + 1

7x − 14

26

7 The velocity, v, of a particle is given by the formula

$$v = u + 17t$$

where u is its initial velocity and t is the time taken. Its velocity reaches four times its initial velocity when $t = 6$ seconds. Find its initial velocity in m/s.

8 Find the actual length and width of this rectangle.

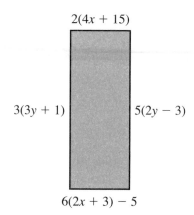

$2(4x + 15)$

$3(3y + 1)$ $5(2y - 3)$

$6(2x + 3) - 5$

TASK E2.8   **Main Book Page 50**

Solve these equations.

1 $\dfrac{x}{4} - 2 = 1$ **2** $\dfrac{1}{2}x + 4 = 9$ **3** $\dfrac{1}{5}x - 2 = 4$

4 $10 = \dfrac{1}{8}x + 3$ **5** $\dfrac{x}{9} + 12 = 15$ **6** $3 = \dfrac{1}{6}x - 5$

7 $\dfrac{x + 9}{4} = 7$ **8** $\dfrac{x - 10}{3} = 6$ **9** $\dfrac{4x - 7}{5} = 5$

10 Elliot writes $\dfrac{6}{x} - 8 = 4$

$$\dfrac{6}{x} = 12$$

$$x = \dfrac{12}{6} = 2$$

Explain what Elliot has done incorrectly and how you would know his answer is wrong.

Solve these equations.

11 $\dfrac{64}{x} = 8$ **12** $11 = \dfrac{12}{x} + 9$ **13** $\dfrac{6x + 2}{11} = 4$

14 $\dfrac{9}{x} + 2 = 4$ **15** $\dfrac{1}{7}x + 8 = 11$ **16** $4 = \dfrac{5}{x} - 3$

17 $\dfrac{3x - 6}{3} = 6$ **18** $8 + \dfrac{4}{x} = 13$ **19** $\dfrac{1}{6}x + 9 = 3$

TASK M2.10 ——————————————————————— **Main Book Page 51**

Factorise the following.

1 $x^2 + 12x + 35$ **2** $m^2 + 12m + 27$ **3** $y^2 - 4y + 3$

4 $n^2 - 2n - 24$ **5** $a^2 - 6a - 27$ **6** $c^2 - 8c - 20$

7 $n^2 - 11n + 24$ **8** $y^2 - 14y + 45$ **9** $a^2 + a - 30$

10 $x^2 - x - 72$ **11** $p^2 + 15p + 44$ **12** $m^2 + 4m - 60$

13 $a^2 - 15a + 56$ **14** $q^2 + 4q - 96$ **15** $b^2 - 5b - 150$

16 $x^2 + 4x + 4 = (x + 2)(x + 2) = (x + 2)^2$
    Write $x^2 + 2x + 1$ in the form $(x + a)^2$. Write down the value of a.

17 Write $x^2 + 8x + 16$ in the form $(x + b)^2$. Write down the value of b.

18 Write $x^2 - 6x + 9$ in the form $(x - c)^2$. Write down the value of c.

19 Write $x^2 - 14x + 49$ in the form $(x - d)^2$. Write down the value of d.

Collect like terms then factorise:

20 $3x^2 + 9x - 2(2x + 1) - 2x^2 + 8$ **21** $x(x + 3) + 3 - x(x + 5) + x(x - 2) - 15$

22 The area of rectangle ABCD
    is $x^2 - 2x - 24$.
    Alex says that an expression
    for the length of AB is $(x - 4)$.
    Explain clearly whether Alex
    is correct or not.

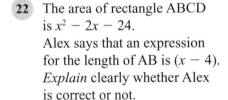

TASK M2.11 ——————————————————————— **Main Book Page 52**

> **Remember:** $A^2 - B^2 = (A + B)(A - B)$
> Difference of 2 squares

Factorise:

1 $x^2 - y^2$ **2** $b^2 - 3^2$ **3** $y^2 - 5^2$ **4** $a^2 - 64$

5 $n^2 - 4$ **6** $p^2 - 1$ **7** $36 - x^2$ **8** $9y^2 - z^2$

9 $49 - 4a^2$ **10** $49x^2 - 81y^2$ **11** $144m^2 - 25$ **12** $16b^2 - \dfrac{1}{9}$

Copy and complete:

13 $5x^2 - 20$
$= \square(x^2 - 4)$
$= \square(x + \square)(x - \square)$

14 $12a^2 - 27b^2$
$= 3(\square - \square)$
$= 3(\square + \square)(\square - \square)$

15 $4m^2 - 8m - 60$
$= 4(m^2 - \square - \square)$
$= 4(m + \square)(m - \square)$

Factorise completely:

16 $3n^2 - 48$

17 $50 - 2b^2$

18 $5t^2 + 15t + 10$

19 $6n^2 - 42n + 60$

20 $12p^2 - 147$

21 $4x^2 - 16x - 48$

22 $9\pi^2 - 1$

23 $\frac{1}{4}e^2 - 25$

24 $e^2 - 16\pi^2$

25 Use the difference of 2 squares to evaluate $15 \cdot 7^2 - 4 \cdot 3^2$ without using a calculator.

26 Collect like terms then factorise:
$$3x^2 + 3x + 1 - 2x^2 - x - 10 - 2x$$

27 Factorise $(x + 4)^2 - (x - 4)^2$

NUMBER 2   3

TASK M3.1 ———————————————— **Main Book Page 61**

1 How many minutes longer does it take Denise to complete a job in three-quarters of an hour than Simon who completes the job in five-twelfths of an hour?

2 Faith says that $\frac{4}{5}$ is smaller than $\frac{5}{6}$.
Explain clearly whether she is correct or not.

3 A womens' football team scores 96 goals during one season. Annie Jackson scores $\frac{3}{8}$ of the team's goals and Claire Benson scores $\frac{5}{16}$ of the goals. How many more goals does Annie score than Claire?

4 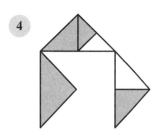 Three congruent triangles are joined together as shown opposite. Parts of the triangles are shaded grey.

One more congruent triangle is added to these triangles. Half of this extra triangle is shaded grey.

What fraction of all the four congruent triangles is shaded grey?

5 Find the difference between $\frac{1}{4}$ and $\frac{2}{5}$, giving the answer as a decimal.

6 $\boxed{\dfrac{35}{40}}$ $\boxed{\dfrac{14}{16}}$ $\boxed{\dfrac{63}{72}}$ $\boxed{\dfrac{140}{160}}$ $\boxed{\dfrac{28}{30}}$ $\boxed{\dfrac{77}{88}}$

Which fractions above are not equivalent to $\frac{7}{8}$?

7 By changing each fraction into a decimal, write the following fractions in order of size, starting with the smallest.

$\boxed{\dfrac{3}{20}}$ $\boxed{\dfrac{1}{4}}$ $\boxed{\dfrac{3}{10}}$ $\boxed{\dfrac{5}{16}}$ $\boxed{\dfrac{3}{25}}$ $\boxed{\dfrac{45}{200}}$

8

plain flour	700 g
butter	450 g
sugar	900 g

Donald users $\frac{3}{5}$ of the flour shown opposite. He also uses $\frac{2}{3}$ of the butter and $\frac{5}{12}$ of the sugar. Write down how much of each item he still has left.

TASK M3.2 ————————————————————— **Main Book Page 63**

1 David writes '$0\cdot35 \neq \dfrac{9}{20}$' ($\neq$ means 'not equal to')

Show clearly whether David is correct.

2 A $\left(3\frac{2}{3} = \frac{11}{3}\right)$ or B $\left(3\frac{2}{3} = \frac{9}{3}\right)$ Which statement is correct?

3 Change the following into mixed numbers.

a $\dfrac{16}{5}$ **b** $\dfrac{27}{7}$ **c** $\dfrac{15}{4}$ **d** $\dfrac{103}{10}$ **e** $\dfrac{53}{8}$

4 Write these numbers in order of size, starting with the smallest.

$\boxed{0\cdot16}$ $\boxed{\dfrac{3}{25}}$ $\boxed{\dfrac{1}{5}}$ $\boxed{0\cdot25}$

5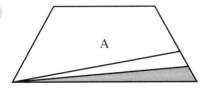

Area A is $\frac{2}{3}$ of the area of a garden. Half of the remaining area is to be used for growing vegetables.

What fraction of the whole garden is to be used for growing vegetables.

6 **a** Write the following decimals in order of size, starting with the *largest*.
0·86, 0·839, 0·087, 0·858, 0·089

b Write out your part **a** answer again but this time insert $\frac{4}{5}$ in its correct position.

7 How many of the statements opposite are true?
Write down the statements which are not true,
explaining clearly why they are not true.

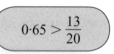

$$0·65 > \frac{13}{20}$$

$$0·65 \neq \frac{13}{20}$$

$$0·65 \geqslant \frac{13}{20}$$

$$0·65 = \frac{13}{20}$$

$$0·65 < \frac{13}{20}$$

8 A geologist has weighed 6 rocks. Their weights are shown below. Work out the difference in
weight between the 5th heaviest rock and the 3rd heaviest rock.

1·2 kg	1·08 kg	1·324 kg
1·29 kg	1·087 kg	1·35 kg

TASK M3.3 ──────────────────────────── **Main Book Page 65**

1 Convert the decimals below into fractions in their lowest form.

a 0·7   **b** 0·35   **c** 0·035   **d** 0·92

e 0·618   **f** 0·3185   **g** 0·713   **h** 0·625

2 Alexa changes $\frac{6}{11}$ into a decimal by dividing 11 into 6. She gets $0·\overset{..}{5}\overset{..}{4}$ (0·545454…)

Show clearly whether she is correct.

3 Use division to convert the fractions below into recurring decimals.

a $\frac{2}{9}$ **b** $\frac{5}{12}$ **c** $\frac{5}{6}$ **d** $\frac{5}{13}$ **e** $\frac{6}{7}$

4 Write these numbers below in order of size, starting with the smallest.

$$\frac{3}{7} \qquad 0{\cdot}427 \qquad 0{\cdot}428$$

5 Work out the value of $\frac{11}{12} + 0{\cdot}087$ without using a calculator.

Give the final answer as a decimal.

TASK M3.4   **Main Book Page 66**

1 Work out and give the answer in its simplest form.

   a $\frac{1}{4} + \frac{2}{3}$ **b** $\frac{5}{6} - \frac{3}{8}$ **c** $\frac{7}{8} - \frac{3}{5}$ **d** $\frac{2}{9} + \frac{3}{7}$

2 Annie and Chad walk from a pub in the same direction. If Annie has walked five-eighths of a mile and Chad had walked seven-tenths of a mile, how far apart are they?

3 Work out and give the answer in its simplest form.

   a $1\frac{2}{3} + 2\frac{1}{2}$ **b** $3\frac{3}{4} + 1\frac{5}{12}$ **c** $5\frac{1}{3} - \frac{7}{8}$ **d** $3\frac{1}{4} - 1\frac{5}{6}$

4

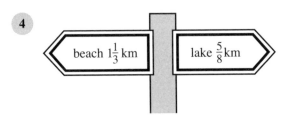

beach $1\frac{1}{3}$ km   lake $\frac{5}{8}$ km

How far apart are the beach and the lake?

5 A bucket contains $4\frac{1}{2}$ litres when full. How much water must Leo add to fill up the bucket completely if it now contains $2\frac{5}{6}$ litres?

6 Work out $\frac{1}{4} + \frac{5}{7} - \frac{3}{8}$

TASK M3.5   **Main Book Page 67**

1 Work out and give the answer in its simplest form:

   a $\frac{5}{8} \times \frac{8}{9}$ **b** $-\frac{7}{12} \times \frac{3}{14}$ **c** $\frac{3}{4} \times 20$ **d** $\frac{3}{5} \div \frac{9}{10}$

   e $-\frac{4}{9} \div \left(-\frac{1}{3}\right)$ **f** $2\frac{1}{2} \times \frac{7}{10}$ **g** $3\frac{1}{3} \times 1\frac{4}{5}$ **h** $-6\frac{1}{4} \div 1\frac{3}{7}$

2 Gary gives $\frac{2}{3}$ of his money to Carol. Carol gives $\frac{6}{7}$ of this money to Zak.
What fraction of Gary's money does Zak get?

3 On a piece of art work, Dennis draws a line which is $\frac{1}{4}$ m long.
He then draws another line which is $\frac{2}{3}$ m long.
What fraction of the second line is the first line?

4 A piece of paper measures $8\frac{1}{4}$ cm by
$7\frac{1}{3}$ cm. A square of side $2\frac{1}{2}$ cm is
cut out and thrown away.
Show that the area that is left
is exactly $54\frac{1}{4}$ cm².

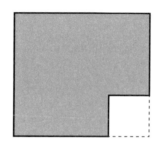

5 A photo measures $7\frac{1}{2}$ cm by $7\frac{1}{5}$ cm. Both its dimensions are increased by a factor of $1\frac{1}{3}$.
Find the area of the enlarged photo.

6 Work out and give the answer in its simplest form:

a $\frac{1}{4} \times \frac{6}{7} + \frac{1}{2}$ **b** $\frac{8}{9} \div \frac{2}{3} - \frac{1}{6}$ **c** $\left(3\frac{2}{3} - 2\frac{3}{5}\right) \div \frac{2}{5}$

7 A piece of metal is $1\frac{2}{3}$ m long. It is heated up so it expands. Its length increases so it is longer
by $\frac{1}{20}$ of its original length.

It is then cooled down. Its length decreases so it is shorter by $\frac{1}{10}$ of its current length.
Work out its final length.

8 Rahul increases the size of his lawn by one-fifth. His lawn now has an area of 108 m².
What was the area of his lawn before he made it larger?

GEOMETRY 1   4

TASK M4.1 ——————————————————————— **Main Book Page 76**

Find the angles marked with letters.

1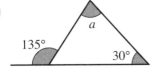

135°   a   30°

2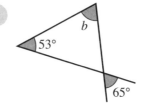

53°   b   65°

3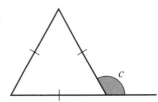

c

4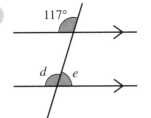

117°   d   e

5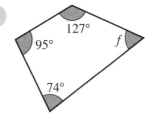

95°   127°   f   74°

6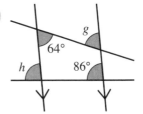

g   64°   h   86°

7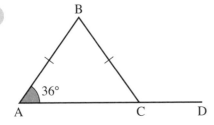

B

36°

A   C   D

Triangle ABC is isosceles.
Work out the value of BĈD, giving reasons
for your answer.

8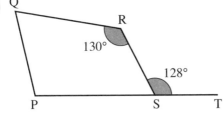

Q   R   130°   128°

P   S   T

PQ̂R = QP̂S
Work out the value of QP̂S, giving reasons
for your answer.

9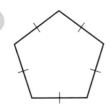

Find the size of an interior angle and an
exterior angle for this regular pentagon.

34

10 Work out the value of PT̂S.

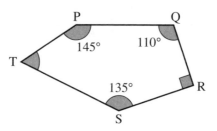

11 The exterior angle of a regular polygon is 45°. How many sides does the polygon have?

12 Work out the value of BĈD in the parallelogram opposite.

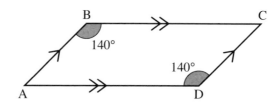

| **TASK M4.2** | **Main Book Page 78** |

1 Which 2 shapes are congruent?

  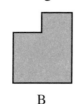  

A   B   C   D   E

2 Copy the diagram opposite.
Enlarge the shape by scale
factor 3 about the centre of
enlargement C.

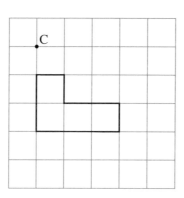

3

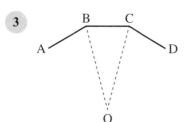

O is the centre of a regular polygon with 20 sides.
ABCD shows 3 sides of the polygon.
Calculate the value of OB̂C.

4

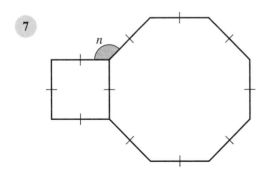

Write down the translation vector which maps

a shape P to shape Q

b shape P to shape R

c shape R to shape Q

5 Work out the value of $A\hat{B}C$ opposite.

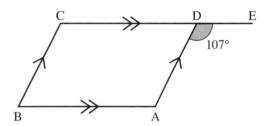

6

P

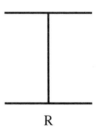

Q

R

a Which two shapes above have the same order of rotational symmetry?

b Write down the order of rotational symmetry for the shapes chosen in part **a**.

7

The diagram opposite shows a square and a regular octagon.
Work out the value of angle n.

8 Copy the shape and mirror line opposite.

   a Reflect shape A in the mirror line.

   b Rotate shape A 180° about the point C.

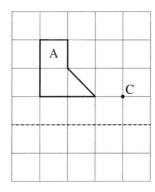

9

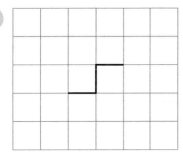

   a Copy the shape opposite onto squared paper.

   b Complete the shape so that it has order of rotational symmetry equal to 4.

10

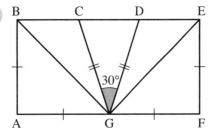

ABEF is a rectangle.
AB = AG = FG = EF
Triangle CDG is isosceles as shown.
Work out the value of DĜE.
Give reasons for your answer.

TASK M4.3   **Main Book Page 81**

1 Prove that triangle QRS is isosceles.
Give all your reasons clearly.

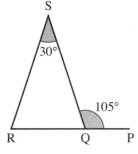

2 ABCD is a square.
Prove that triangle BCD is isosceles.
Give all your reasons clearly.

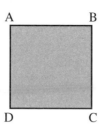

A   B

D   C

3 Prove that triangle QUT is isosceles.
Give all your reasons clearly.

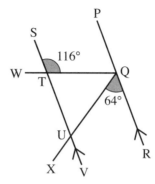

4 Prove that the sum of the angles in a triangle add up to 180°. Give all your reasons clearly.

5 ABCD is a rectangle.
Prove that triangle ABM
is isosceles.
Give all your reasons clearly.

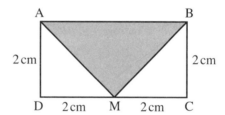

A   B
2 cm   2 cm
D 2 cm M 2 cm C

TASK E4.1   **Main Book Page 82**

1 Express $A\hat{B}C$ in terms of x.

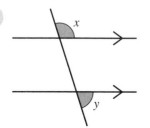

2 Express y in terms of x.

3 Prove that the angles in a regular pentagon add up to 540°.

4 $S\hat{R}Q = S\hat{T}Q$ in the diagram opposite.
Express $R\hat{S}T$ in terms of x.
Andrea writes:
$R\hat{Q}T = 180 - x + 20 = 200 - x$
$S\hat{R}Q = x \, (= S\hat{T}Q)$
$R\hat{S}T = 360 - x - x - 200 - x$
$R\hat{S}T = 160 - 3x$
Sam thinks that Andrea has made mistakes.
Explain clearly what these mistakes are.

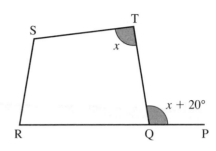

5 Express y in terms of x.

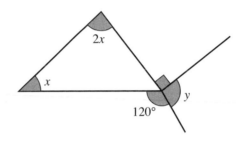

6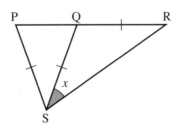

Write down an expression, in terms of n, for the interior angle of a regular polygon with n sides.

7

ABCD is a square.
M, N and P are midpoints of AD, BC and CD respectively.
Express $N\hat{P}Q$ in terms of x.

8 Express $P\hat{S}Q$ in terms of x.

TASK M4.4 ———————————————————————— **Main Book Page 85**

> **Remember:** to prove triangles are congruent, look for SSS, SAS, AAS or RHS

1 *Explain* why these two triangles are congruent.

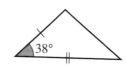

2 *Explain* why these two triangles are *not* congruent.

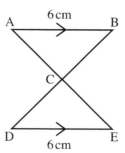

3 AB is parallel to DE.
BC = CD.
Give reasons why
   a $A\hat{B}C = C\hat{D}E$
   b $A\hat{C}B = D\hat{C}E$
   c Explain why triangles ABC and CDE are congruent.

4

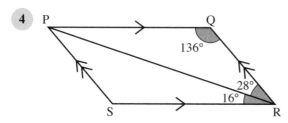

PQRS is a parallelogram.
Find the value of
   a $Q\hat{P}R$. Give a reason.
   b $R\hat{P}S$. Give a reason.
   c $P\hat{S}R$. Give a reason.
   d Explain why triangles PQR and PRS are congruent

5 **a** Prove that triangles ACX and ACY are congruent.
   b *Explain* why AY = CX.

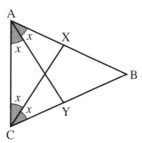

6

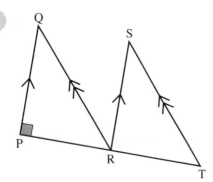

Al writes the following:

'SR̂T = QP̂R = 90° (corresponding angles are equal)

QR̂S = PQ̂R (alternate angles are equal)

RŜT = QR̂S (alternate angles are equal)

so RŜT = PQ̂R

ST̂R = QR̂P (corresponding angles are equal)

so triangles PQR and RST are congruent'.

Freya thinks that Al has made a mistake.

Explain clearly why Freya thinks this.

7 Triangle ABC is isosceles with AB = BC.
M and N are the midpoints of AB and BC respectively.

PQBM and BRSN are both squares.

a Prove that triangles BRM and BNQ are congruent.

b Explain why MR = NQ.

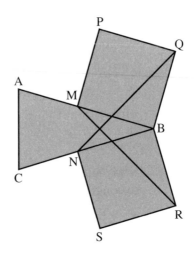

8 PQRS is a kite.
Use congruent triangles to prove that diagonal PR bisects SP̂Q.

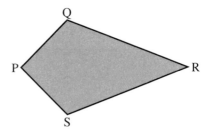

TASK M4.5 — **Main Book Page 88**

1 Copy the grid and shape opposite.

   a Reflect shape A in the *y*-axis.
      Label the image B.

   b Reflect shape B in the *x*-axis.
      Label the image C.

   c Reflect shape C in the line $x = 1$.
      Label the image D.

   d Reflect shape D in the $y = -1.5$.
      Label the image E.

   e Reflect shape E in the *y*-axis.
      Label the image F.

   f Reflect shape F in the line $y = 2$.
      Label the image G.

   g Shape G reflects back onto shape A.
      Write down the name (equation) of
      the line of reflection.

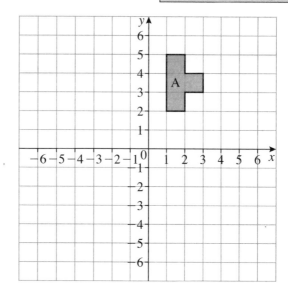

2

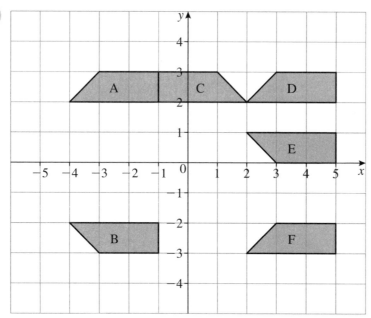

For each pair of shapes below, write down the equation of the *line of reflection.*

   a A to B   **b** A to C   **c** C to D   **d** D to E   **e** E to F

3   **a** Draw an *x*-axis from -4 to 4 and a *y*-axis from -4 to 4.

     b Draw the line $y = x$.

     c Draw any triangle then reflect it in the line $y = x$.

4 **a** Draw an *x*-axis from −5 to 5 and a *y*-axis from −5 to 5.

  b Draw an ⌐-shape A with vertices (−2, 1), (−2, 4), (−4, 4), (−4, 3), (−3, 3) and (−3, 1).

  c Translate shape A through $\begin{pmatrix} 3 \\ 0 \end{pmatrix}$. Label the image B.

  d Reflect shape B in the line *y* = *x*. Label the image C.

  e Translate shape C through $\begin{pmatrix} -1 \\ -2 \end{pmatrix}$. Label the image D.

  f Shape D is reflected back onto shape A. Write down the equation of the *line of reflection*.

TASK M4.6/M4.7	Main Book Page 91

> **Remember:** to describe a rotation *fully*, give
> 1 the angle
> 2 the direction (clockwise or anticlockwise)
> 3 the centre of rotation

You may want to use tracing paper.

1 Find the co-ordinates of the centres of the following rotations:

  a shape A onto shape B

  b shape B onto shape C

  c shape C onto shape D

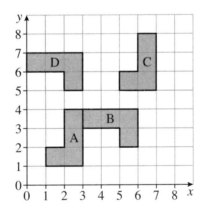

2 Describe *fully* the rotation which transforms:

  a triangle A onto triangle B

  b triangle C onto triangle D

  c triangle B onto triangle C

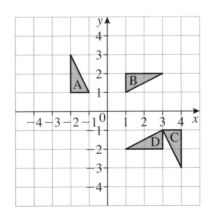

3

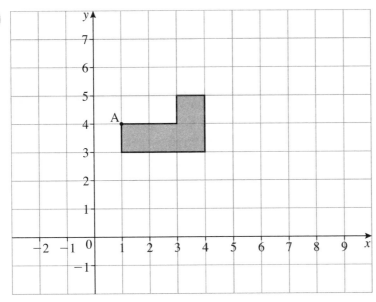

a Copy the axes and shape above.

b Reflect this shape in the line $y = 2$ and write down the new co-ordinates of vertex A.

c Rotate the shape opposite 180° about (5, 5). Write down the new co-ordinates of vertex A.

4　**a** Describe *fully* the rotation which moves shape A onto shape B.

b Describe *fully* the translation which moves shape B onto shape C.

c Describe *fully* the rotation which moves shape C onto shape A.

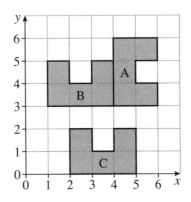

TASK M4.8 ———————————————————————— **Main Book Page 95**

1　**a** Draw the *x*-axis from −6 to 10.
Draw the *y*-axis from −4 to 5.
Draw shape A with vertices at (−2, 2), (−2, 3), (−1, 3), (−1, 4), (−4, 4), (−4, 3), (−3, 3), (−3, 2).

b Enlarge shape A by scale factor 3 about (−3, 5). Label the image B.

c Enlarge shape B by scale factor $\frac{1}{3}$ about (9, −1). Label the image C.

d Look at the vertex (−2, 2) in shape A. Write down the co-ordinates of the same vertex in shape C.

In questions **2** and **3**, draw the grid and the 2 shapes then draw broken lines through pairs of points in the new shape and the old shape. Describe *fully* the enlargement which transforms shape A onto shape B.

2
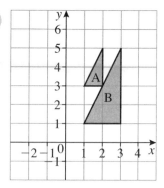

3
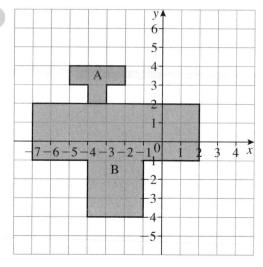

4
  a Draw an *x*-axis from -7 to 7 and a *y*-axis from -7 to 7.

  b Draw a rectangle P with vertices at $(-1, -2), (-1, -3), (-3, -3)$ and $(-3, -2)$.

  c Enlarge rectangle P by scale factor 2 about $(0, 0)$. Label the image Q.

  d Translate rectangle Q through $\binom{8}{3}$. Label the image R.

  e Enlarge rectangle R by scale factor 2 about $(6, -7)$. Label the image S.

  f Enlarge rectangle S by scale factor $\frac{1}{4}$ about $(-6, 5)$. Label the image T.

  g Describe fully the transformation which maps T onto P.

TASK M4.9   **Main Book Page 97**

You may want to use tracing paper.

1 Describe *fully* the transformation which moves:

  a triangle A onto triangle B

  b triangle B onto triangle C

  c triangle C onto triangle D

  d triangle D onto triangle E

  e triangle D onto triangle F

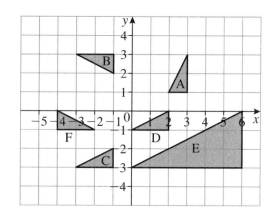

2 **a** Draw the *x*-axis from −5 to 5.
Draw the *y*-axis from −6 to 6.
Draw shape A with vertices at (−2, 2),
(−4, 2), (−4, 4), (−2, 6).

b Enlarge shape A by scale factor $\frac{1}{2}$ about
the origin. Label the image B.

c Reflect shape B in the line $y = -1$.
Label the image C.

d Rotate shape C 90° anticlockwise about
(−2, −2). Label the image D.

e Translate shape D through $\begin{pmatrix} 3 \\ 4 \end{pmatrix}$.
Label the image E.

f Rotate shape E 90° clockwise about (2, 2).
Label the image F.

g Describe *fully* the transformation that
would move shape F onto shape C.

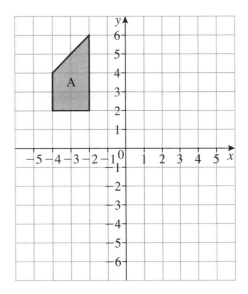

| **TASK M4.10** | **Main Book Page 100** |

1 Write each vector as a column vector, eg. $\overrightarrow{CD} = \begin{pmatrix} 1 \\ -1 \end{pmatrix}$

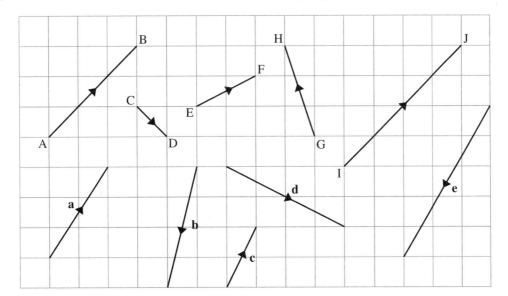

2 Draw and label each vector below on squared paper.

$$\mathbf{f} = \begin{pmatrix} 4 \\ -1 \end{pmatrix} \qquad \mathbf{g} = \begin{pmatrix} 2 \\ 2 \end{pmatrix} \qquad \mathbf{h} = \begin{pmatrix} -3 \\ -2 \end{pmatrix} \qquad \overrightarrow{PQ} = \begin{pmatrix} -2 \\ 0 \end{pmatrix} \qquad \overrightarrow{XY} = \begin{pmatrix} -5 \\ 2 \end{pmatrix}$$

3 Draw the vector $\begin{pmatrix} n \\ 8 \end{pmatrix}$ so that its length is 10 units. You must work out what value of n is to be used. State this value of n.

TASK M4.11 ──────────────────────────────── **Main Book Page 103**

1 If $\mathbf{k} = \begin{pmatrix} 2 \\ 4 \end{pmatrix}$, $\mathbf{m} = \begin{pmatrix} -3 \\ 2 \end{pmatrix}$ and $\mathbf{n} = \begin{pmatrix} -5 \\ -1 \end{pmatrix}$, find as a single column vector:

a $3\mathbf{m}$ **b** $4\mathbf{n}$ **c** $\mathbf{m} + \mathbf{k}$ **d** $2\mathbf{m} + \mathbf{n}$

e $5\mathbf{k} - \mathbf{n}$ **f** $2\mathbf{k} + 3\mathbf{m} + 2\mathbf{n}$ **g** $4(\mathbf{m} - \mathbf{n})$ **h** $\frac{1}{2}(\mathbf{k} + 2\mathbf{n})$

2 Give each of the following as a single column vector.

a $\begin{pmatrix} 2 \\ 6 \end{pmatrix} + 3\begin{pmatrix} 1 \\ 4 \end{pmatrix}$ **b** $\begin{pmatrix} 8 \\ 6 \end{pmatrix} - \begin{pmatrix} 4 \\ -2 \end{pmatrix}$ **c** $\begin{pmatrix} 2 \\ -3 \end{pmatrix} - 3\begin{pmatrix} 4 \\ -1 \end{pmatrix}$

d $5\begin{pmatrix} 3 \\ 4 \end{pmatrix} + 2\begin{pmatrix} 2 \\ 3 \end{pmatrix}$ **e** $6\begin{pmatrix} 3 \\ -2 \end{pmatrix} - 2\begin{pmatrix} -1 \\ -5 \end{pmatrix}$ **f** $\begin{pmatrix} 6 \\ -2 \end{pmatrix} + \frac{1}{3}\begin{pmatrix} 12 \\ 9 \end{pmatrix}$

3 **a** Draw an x-axis from -4 to 4 and a y-axis from -4 to 4.

    b Mark a cross at the point P $(-2, 1)$.

    c Mark the point Q such that $\overrightarrow{PQ} = \begin{pmatrix} 3 \\ -4 \end{pmatrix}$

    d Mark the point R such that $\overrightarrow{PR} = \begin{pmatrix} 5 \\ 2 \end{pmatrix}$

    e Write down the value of $\overrightarrow{RQ}$ as a column vector.

    f Write down $\overrightarrow{PR} + \overrightarrow{RQ}$ as a single column vector.

4 Find the value of n in each statement below:

a $\begin{pmatrix} 3 \\ n \end{pmatrix} + \begin{pmatrix} 2 \\ 3 \end{pmatrix} = \begin{pmatrix} 5 \\ 1 \end{pmatrix}$ **b** $\begin{pmatrix} 6 \\ 7 \end{pmatrix} - 3\begin{pmatrix} n \\ 2 \end{pmatrix} = \begin{pmatrix} -3 \\ 1 \end{pmatrix}$

c $\begin{pmatrix} 8 \\ 5 \end{pmatrix} + n\begin{pmatrix} 2 \\ -4 \end{pmatrix} = \begin{pmatrix} 18 \\ -15 \end{pmatrix}$ **d** $4\begin{pmatrix} 2 \\ n \end{pmatrix} - 5\begin{pmatrix} 1 \\ -3 \end{pmatrix} = \begin{pmatrix} 3 \\ 39 \end{pmatrix}$

5 $\overrightarrow{AB} = \begin{pmatrix} 1 \\ -2 \end{pmatrix}$. $\overrightarrow{CD}$ is twice as large as $\overrightarrow{AB}$ but points in the opposite direction. Write down the value of $\overrightarrow{CD}$ as a column vector.

TASK E4.2 ———————————————————————————

1 Look at the diagram opposite.
We can see that $\overrightarrow{AF} = \overrightarrow{CD}$.
Write down a column vector equal to:

a $\overrightarrow{DE}$

b $\overrightarrow{BE} + \overrightarrow{EF}$

c $\overrightarrow{AF} + \overrightarrow{FE}$

d $\overrightarrow{ED} + \overrightarrow{DC}$

e $\overrightarrow{BC} + \overrightarrow{CD} + \overrightarrow{DE}$

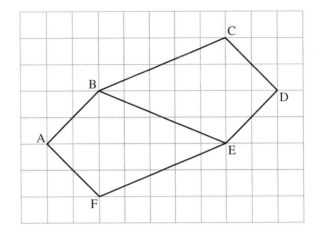

2 Make a copy of this grid then write on the letters A to H so that:

a $\overrightarrow{OA} = 2\mathbf{a}$ **b** $\overrightarrow{OB} = \mathbf{a} + 2\mathbf{b}$

c $\overrightarrow{OC} = -\mathbf{b}$ **d** $\overrightarrow{OD} = 2\mathbf{a} - 2\mathbf{b}$

e $\overrightarrow{OE} = -2\mathbf{a} + \mathbf{b}$ **f** $\overrightarrow{OF} = -\mathbf{a} - \mathbf{b}$

g $\overrightarrow{OG} = -2\mathbf{a} - 2\mathbf{b}$ **h** $\overrightarrow{OH} = 2\mathbf{a} + 3\mathbf{b}$

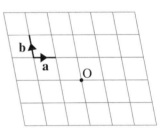

3 Look at the diagram in question **1**. Calculate the length of vector $\overrightarrow{AB}$.

4 Calculate the length of vector $\overrightarrow{BC}$ in question **1**.

5 The length of a vector is known as its *modulus*.
Draw each vector below on squared paper then calculate the modulus of each vector.

a $\begin{pmatrix} 3 \\ 4 \end{pmatrix}$ **b** $\begin{pmatrix} 9 \\ 12 \end{pmatrix}$ **c** $\begin{pmatrix} 10 \\ 24 \end{pmatrix}$ **d** $\begin{pmatrix} 1 \\ 1 \end{pmatrix}$

TASK E4.3 ———————————————————————————

1 Express each vector in terms of **a**, **b** or **c**.

a $\overrightarrow{AC}$ **b** $\overrightarrow{CA}$ **c** $\overrightarrow{AD}$ **d** $\overrightarrow{BD}$

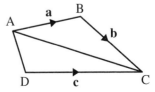

48

2 KLMN is a rhombus.
Express each vector in terms of **m** and **n**.

   a $\overrightarrow{KN}$ **b** $\overrightarrow{MN}$ **c** $\overrightarrow{LN}$ **d** $\overrightarrow{MK}$

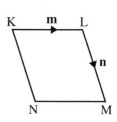

3 M has co-ordinates (3, 1)

$\overrightarrow{MN} = \begin{pmatrix} 4 \\ 2 \end{pmatrix}$ and $\overrightarrow{MP} = \begin{pmatrix} 3 \\ -1 \end{pmatrix}$.

   a Find the co-ordinates of N.

   b Find the co-ordinates of P.

   c Find $\overrightarrow{NP}$ as a column vector.

4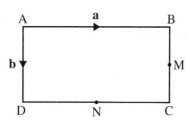

ABCD is a rectangle.
$\overrightarrow{AB} = \mathbf{a}$ and $\overrightarrow{AD} = \mathbf{b}$.
M is the midpoint of BC and N is the midpoint of CD.

Express the following vectors in terms of **a** and **b**.

   a $\overrightarrow{AM}$ **b** $\overrightarrow{AN}$ **c** $\overrightarrow{BN}$ **d** $\overrightarrow{MN}$

5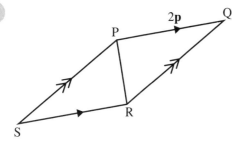

PQRS is a parallelogram,

$\overrightarrow{PQ} = 2\mathbf{p}$

If $\overrightarrow{PR} = 2\mathbf{p} + \mathbf{q}$, express vector $\overrightarrow{SP}$ in terms of **p** and **q**.

6 $\overrightarrow{KL} = \begin{pmatrix} 2 \\ 5 \end{pmatrix}$ and $\overrightarrow{MN} = \begin{pmatrix} 8 \\ 20 \end{pmatrix}$

KL is parallel to MN. *Explain* why.

NUMBER 3   5

Main Book Page 115

TASK M5.1

1 **a** Copy and complete the factor tree opposite:

   b Write down 135 as a product of its prime factors.

   c Write down 315 as a product of its prime factors.

   d Write down the Highest Common Factor (HCF) of 135 and 315.

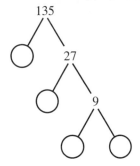

2 Write down two numbers which add to make -7 and multiply to make 12.

3 Which gives the larger answer: $(-4)^2$ or $(-4)^3$? Explain your answer fully.

4 John and Stella share a flat. Part of their most recent electricity bill is shown below.

   > Previous reading   34189
   > Present reading   35153
   > VAT 5%
   > 16p per unit of electricity

   Stella pays one-fifth of the bill. How much does she pay?

5 Roman sells 26 car radios for £884 during one month. The following month he sells 37 car radios. Find out how much he receives for the 37 car radios without using a calculator.

6 The sixth square number is subtracted from the fourth square number. This answer is then subtracted from the third highest cube number. Write down the final answer.

7 Which answer below is the greater and by how much?

   A $(-4 + 2)^2$ or   B $-4 + (5 - 6)^2$

8 Write down a number which is odd, square and a factor of 36.

9 Find the missing value ? in the sum below:

   $6 - \boxed{?} - 4 + 2 = 8$

1 $\frac{6}{7} \times \boxed{?} = \frac{2}{3}$ Find the value of the missing fraction.

2 Answer true or false for each of the following:

   a $\frac{9}{25} = 0\!\cdot\!36$ **b** $\frac{1}{8} = 0\!\cdot\!8$ **c** $\frac{18}{50} = 0\!\cdot\!18$

   d $0\!\cdot\!24 = \frac{6}{25}$ **e** $\frac{13}{100} = 0\!\cdot\!13$ **f** $0\!\cdot\!45 = \frac{9}{20}$

3 Find the difference between $1\!\cdot\!6 \times 10^5$ and $3\!\cdot\!9 \times 10^4$.

4 A piece of wood is $\frac{3}{4}$ m long. Molly cuts a small section of wood off this piece which leaves $\frac{3}{5}$ m. What length of wood did Molly cut off?

5 Aryan says that $4\!\cdot\!6 \times 10^{-3}$ is greater than $0\!\cdot\!037$. Anna disagrees.
   Explain clearly who is correct.

6 Gianna has 240 hats to sell during a carnival. She sells $\frac{3}{8}$ of the hats during the first 2 hours.
   A friend then takes $\frac{2}{3}$ of the remaining hats to sell in his shop. During the final hour she sells $\frac{9}{10}$ of the remaining hats at £9 each. How much money does she take during the final hour?

7 A $\boxed{\quad 6 + 4 \times 2 \quad}$ B $\boxed{\quad 2 \times 7 + 3 \times 2 \quad}$

   C $\boxed{\quad 4 \times (7 - 2) \quad}$ D $\boxed{\quad 30 - 2 \times 5 \quad}$

   Only one of the above questions does *not* give the answer 20.
   Write down which question this is. Justify your answer.

8 Work out

   a $-\frac{4}{5} \times -\frac{10}{11}$ **b** $\frac{2}{5} + \frac{3}{7}$ **c** $\frac{3}{8} \times -48$ **d** $5\frac{1}{2} - 1\frac{5}{6}$

9 Write the number 21700 in standard form.

10 Work out the value of $-\frac{3}{8} - \frac{2}{9}$.

   What number must be added to this answer to make the result equal 2?

TASK M5.3 ———————————————————————————— **Main Book Page 119**

1 1 890 000 people vote for the Green party in a General Election. Five years later in the next General Election, the number of people who vote for the Green party decreases by 8%. At a final General Election another five years later, the number of people voting for the Green party increases by 11% on the previous General Election. How many people voted for the Green party in this final General Election?

2 Without using a calculator decide which of the following answers are correct:

a $0.6 \times 4 = 0.24$

b $16 - 2.18 = 13.82$

c $1.7 + 12.46 = 12.63$

d $0.07 \times 0.8 = 0.056$

3 Whilst in Los Angeles in the USA, Aiden buys a small jacket for $89·46. He then travels to Berlin in Germany and buys an identical jacket for €70·20. Use the exchange rates opposite to work out which jacket was cheaper and by how much (in £'s)?

£1 = $1·42

£1 = €1·17

4 Use a calculator to work out each of the following questions, giving each answer to 3 significant figures.

$$\sqrt{(4.3^2 + 2.89)}$$

$$\frac{6.02}{0.15} - 2.01^2$$

$$\frac{5.3 + 4.68^2}{9.37^2 - 40.8}$$

Show that the sum of the second digits in each answer is 24.

$$\frac{2.57^3}{1.03 + 0.96^2}$$

5 A coat costs £60 after a 25% reduction in a sale. What was the price of the coat before the reduction?

6 Jasper has £1600. 40% of the money is used for his rent. He saves and spends the remaining money in the ratio $3:2$. He finds a bike he wants to buy for £445. Can he afford to buy the bike or does he need to use some of his saved money? Show all your working out clearly.

7 Dale says that the answer to $\sqrt{3\cdot6} + \dfrac{1\cdot8}{0\cdot7}$ is 4·46 correct to 3 significant figures.

Huan says that Dale has made a mistake. Explain clearly whether Huan is correct or not.

8 Kate borrows £4000 to buy a car. She is charged simple interest at 5% per annum.
She pays back *all* the money in monthly instalments over 4 years.
How much is each monthly instalment?

9

$AB : BC = 5 : 2$

What fraction of the
line AC is line AB?

10 The table opposite shows
whether some people like
chinese food or not.

	Yes	No
Female	12	2
Male	7	4

   a What percentage of the
people asked are male?

   b What is the ratio of females to males who do not like chinese food?

   c What percentage of the females like chinese food? Give the answer to one decimal place.

TASK M5.4 ———————————————————————— **Main Book Page 122**

Do not use a calculator.

1 Copy the questions below and fill in the empty boxes.

   a $13\cdot2 \div 0\cdot4 = 132 \div 4 = \boxed{}$

   b $5\cdot84 \div 0\cdot2 = 58\cdot4 \div \boxed{} = \boxed{}$

   c $7\cdot1 \div 0\cdot02 = 710 \div \boxed{} = \boxed{}$

   d $15\cdot6 \div 0\cdot02 = \boxed{} \div 2 = \boxed{}$

2 Work out:

   a $1\cdot35 \div 0\cdot3$ **b** $6\cdot8 \div 0\cdot2$ **c** $3\cdot36 \div 0\cdot6$

   d $0\cdot192 \div 0\cdot4$ **e** $0\cdot215 \div 0\cdot05$ **f** $0\cdot504 \div 0\cdot08$

3 A bottle contains 0·12 litres of medicine. A teaspoon holds 0·005 litres.
How many teaspoons of medicine can be taken from the bottle?

4 Copy and complete the number chains below:

   a $\boxed{6\cdot2} \rightarrow \boxed{\times\ 0\cdot4} \rightarrow \boxed{} \rightarrow \boxed{\div\ 0\cdot02} \rightarrow \boxed{} \rightarrow \boxed{\div\ 0\cdot8} \rightarrow \boxed{}$

   b $\boxed{0\cdot348} \rightarrow \boxed{\div\ 0\cdot06} \rightarrow \boxed{} \rightarrow \boxed{\div\ 0\cdot2} \rightarrow \boxed{} \rightarrow \boxed{\div\ 0\cdot4} \rightarrow \boxed{}$

   c $\boxed{0\cdot485} \rightarrow \boxed{\div\ 0\cdot05} \rightarrow \boxed{} \rightarrow \boxed{\times\ 0\cdot6} \rightarrow \boxed{} \rightarrow \boxed{\div\ 0\cdot3} \rightarrow \boxed{}$

5 The area of the triangle opposite is $0.24 \, m^2$. Work out the value of h.

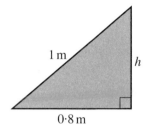

1 m

h

0·8 m

6 $8 \div 0.5 = 16$ and $1.6 \div 0.5 = 3.2$
Explain why the quickest way to divide a number by 0·5 is to double the number?

7 Put the answers to the questions below in order of size, starting with the smallest.

$0.06 \div 0.4$	0.9×0.2	$0.4 \div 8$	$0.006 \div 0.05$
A	B	C	D

TASK M5.5/M5.6 ———————————————— **Main Book Page 124**

Use a calculator when needed. Give answers to one decimal place if necessary.

1 Ryan buys a mobile for £240 and sells it one year later for £204.
What was his percentage loss?

2 Kelly buys a car for £300 and works on it before selling it for £420.
What was the percentage profit?

3 A supermarket increases its workforce from 90 people to 117 people.
What is the percentage increase?

4 Find the percentage increase or decrease for each of the following:

a | original amount = 360   final amount = 514·8

b | original amount = 672   final amount = 564·48

c | original amount = 32   final amount = 62·4

5 Leanne buys 100 books for £450. She sells each book for £5·40.
Find the percentage profit Leanne makes on the books.

6 Sam buys 70 scarves at £5 each. He sells 40 of the scarves for £11 each but fails to sell the other scarves. Find the percentage profit he makes.

7 Joe buys a flat for £70 000 and sells it for £85 000.
Mo buys a house for £192 000 and sells it for £230 000.
Who makes the larger percentage profit and by how much?

8 The length, width and height of this cuboid are each increased by 15%.
What is the percentage increase in the volume of this cuboid?

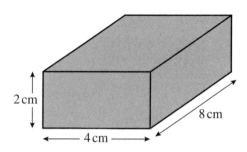

9 The price of a TV is increased by 30% then the new price is decreased by 30%.
What is the overall percentage change to the original price of the TV?

10 Last year 160 students out of 240 in Year 11 in Henton High School attained a grade 4 or above in their Maths GCSE. This year there was a 10% increase in the number of people gaining a grade 4 or above for GCSE Maths. The number of students in Year 11 increased by 5% compared to last year. Work out the percentage increase in the pass rate this year compared to last year for students in Year 11 gaining a grade 4 or above in GCSE Maths.

11 Sandra's ideal body weight is 57 kg. During a period of six months her weight increases by 10%. During the next three months her weight returns to its ideal 57 kg. What was the percentage decrease from her heaviest weight back to her ideal weight?

| **TASK M5.7** | **Main Book Page 127** |

Use a calculator when needed.

1 Ron's height has increased by 5% over the last year. He is now 1·89 m tall.
How tall was he one year ago?

2 Katy now pays £129·60 rent each week after an 8% rent increase.
How much did she pay before the increase?

3 One week Arlene spends £75·60 on food which is 18% of her weekly pay.
How much is her weekly pay?

4 A bike costs £408 including VAT at 20%.
How much did the bike cost before VAT was added?

5 46 students from Year 10 in Grove Park School are ill one day.
If this is 28·75% of all the Year 10 pupils, how many students are there in Year 10 in total?

6

| DVD player £61 including VAT | In which shop is the DVD player cheaper and by how much? (VAT is 20%) | DVD player £52 + VAT |

HOBBS ELECTRICS   HEFTON'S

7 Mark collects teapots. He now has 45 teapots which is 25% more than he had one year ago. How many teapots did he have one year ago?

8 The value of Chloe's house has dropped by 8% since she bought it and is now worth £211 600. How much did Chloe pay for the house?

| **TASK E5.1** | **Main Book Page 128** |

1 Council Tax is increased by 3% each year for two consecutive years. The Harris family pay £1350 in the year after the two rises. How much did they pay two years earlier?

2 The number of people working in a factory in 2013 drops 20% by 2014. This number then increases 25% by the year 2015. In 2015 there are 90 people working in the factory. What overall percentage change in the number of people has taken place between 2013 and 2015?

3 Don answers the following question:

'A computer is sold for £1200 at a loss of 20%. How much was the computer originally bought for?'

Don answers as follows:

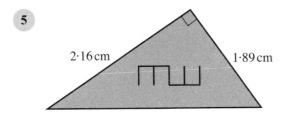

Loss is 20% of £1200 = 0·2 × 1200 = £240
Original price = 1200 + 240 = £1440

Explain clearly the mistakes in Don's answer.

4 The price of a barrel of oil falls 14% then increases by 10%. The current price is £96·49 per barrel. What was the price of a barrel before the two percentage changes?

5

2·16 cm   1·89 cm

A company increases the size of its logo opposite.
The base of the triangle is increased by 8% to 2·16 cm. The height of the triangle is increased by 5% to 1·89 cm. What was the area of the logo triangle before its size was increased?

6 I invest some money. It makes 2% of its value at the start of each year for 3 consecutive years. It then makes 3% of its value at the start of each year for a further 3 consecutive years. I then have £3478·83 invested. How much money did I invest at the start?

7 A cube is coated with a varnish which increases the length of each side by 1%. The volume of the cube including varnish is now 222·545016 cm³. What was the volume of the original cube?

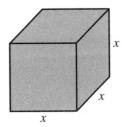

TASK M5.8 ───────────────────────────── **Main Book Page 130**

Use a calculator when needed. Give answers to the nearest penny if necessary.

1 Tina invests £8000 in a bank at 5% per annum (year) compound interest.
How much money will she have in the bank after 2 years?

2 A motorbike loses 25% of its value every year. Jennifer bought it for £720.
How much would it be worth after:
a 2 years   **b** 3 years

3 Which of the following will earn more money in 2 years?
A £4000 at 5·6% p.a. *simple* interest   *or*   **B** £4000 at 5·5% p.a. compound interest

4 A country has a population of 7 300 000.
The population decreases by 2% each year for the next two years.
What is the size of the population after these two years?

5

RETURN CO
3·8% per annum compound interest

SMART BANK
3% for Year 1   4·5% for Year 2

Tariq invests £5500 in Return Co for 2 years.
Julie invests £5500 in Smart Bank for 2 years.
Who gains the most interest and by how much?

6 Tom buys a car for £8000. It loses 20% of its value every year. Louise has £4000 when Tom buys his car. She invests her money at 4% per annum compound interest. After how many years would she be able to afford to buy Tom's car? Show all your working out.

TASK E5.2 ───────────────────────────── **Main Book Page 132**

Remember: 'increase by 12%' means 'multiply by 1·12'
1·12 is the *percentage multiplier*

1 A building society offers 8% p.a. compound interest. Candice puts £560 into the building society.
a Write down the *percentage multiplier* which could be used to find out how much money is in the building society after 1 year.
b How much money would be in the building society after 5 years?

2 The value of a bike depreciates (goes down) by 10% of its value each year.
Richard buys a new bike for £750.
a Write down the *percentage multiplier* which could be used to find out the value of the bike after 1 year.
b How much will Richard's bike be worth after 6 years?

3

Supa Save
4% per annum compound interest plus 2% bonus at the end of 3 years

Mega Money
4·5% per annum compound interest

Robert has £15 000 to invest for 3 years.
Which account above will give him more money and by how much?

4 In a large town, 30 000 people get their gas supply from Central Gas.
10 000 people get their gas from Gas Centric.
By the end of each year, Central Gas loses 10% of its customers at the start of the year and Gas Centric gains 15% of its customers at the start of the year. During which year does Gas Centric first have more customers than Central Gas? *Explain* your answer fully.

5 Vikram invests some money in a bank at 12% p.a. compound interest.
After how many years will his money have trebled?

6 Mrs Jones is 65 years old. She has worked out that due to inflation her savings will lose 5% of their value at the start of each year by the end of that year.
How old will she be by the end of the first year in which her savings are worth less than half of their current value?

7 Arya invests some money at 3·5% per annum compound interest. He wants to have saved £10 000 after 10 years. What is the least amount of money he must invest to ensure that he reaches this target after 10 years?

TASK M5.9 ────────────────────────────── **Main Book Page 135**

1 Change the following ratios to their simplest form, i.e. where both numbers are integers (whole numbers).

 a $0·3 : 0·05$ 　　　 **b** $\dfrac{4}{5} : \dfrac{1}{3}$ 　　　 **c** $0·2 : \dfrac{3}{5}$ 　　　 **d** $\dfrac{2}{7} : \dfrac{3}{4}$

2 Des, Simone and Julie earn money in the ratio $3 : 2 : 5$. If Des earns £9000 per year more than Simone, how much does Julie earn each year?

3 m is $\dfrac{3}{8}$ of n. Write down the ratio $m : n$.

4

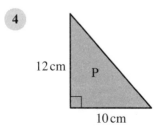

The ratio of the areas of triangle P to square Q is $3 : 5$. Work out the length of one side of square Q.

5 5 litres of antifreeze and water are mixed together in the ratio 1 : 3.
How much water must be added to make the ratio 1 : 5?

6 The recipe for making 20 biscuits is given below:

120 g	butter
50 g	caster sugar
175 g	flour

Helen has 300 g butter, 200 g caster sugar
and 525 g flour. What is the maximum
number of biscuits she can make?

7 The area of a garden is 40 m². It is split into a lawn and flower beds in the ratio 4 : 1.
Eva decides to grow vegetables so splits the lawn into a vegetable patch and lawn in
the ratio 2 : 3. Work out the area of the vegetable patch.

8 PQ : QR : RS = 7 : 3 : 8
If PQ is 10 cm longer than QR,
what is the length of line PS?

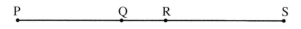

9 Payton has savings in a bank and more in a building society. The amount is in the ratio 4 : 7.
She has £7500 more in the building society. Payton takes £2500 out of the building society.
Work out the new ratio for the amount of money she has in the bank compared to the building
society. Give the ratio in its simplest form.

10 Some money is shared between Jess and Ryan in the ratio 5 : 8. If Jess gets £n less than Ryan,
how much money does Ryan get (give the answer in terms of n)?

TASK M5.10 ──────────────────────────── **Main Book Page 138**

1 P is directly proportional to Q.
$P = 60$ when $Q = 10$. Find the value of P when
a $Q = 5$ **b** $Q = 20$ **c** $Q = 25$

2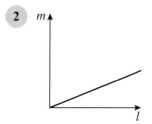

Chris says that the mass m of a metal bar
is directly proportional to its length l.
Does the graph opposite support his
statement? Explain your answer fully.

3 p is directly proportional to q.
$p = 28$ when $q = 4$.
Find
a p when $q = 9$ **b** q when $p = 21$

4 $16\,\text{m}^2$ of carpet costs £383·84. How much carpet can be bought for £527·78?

5 Which equations below suggest that y is directly proportional to x?

  a $y = \dfrac{3}{x}$ **b** $y = 7x$ **c** $\dfrac{y}{4} = x$ **d** $y = 3x^2$ **e** $y = \dfrac{1}{2}x$

6 In an electrical circuit it is known that the voltage V varies as the current I (i.e. that V is directly proportional to I). It is also known that $V = 36$ when $I = 9$.

  a $V = kI$. Show that $V = 4I$.   **b** Find V when $I = 7$.
  c Find I when $V = 81$.   **d** Find V when $I = 11\cdot5$.

7 Write down any equation which you believe is appropriate for the relationship shown by the graph opposite.

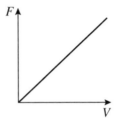

8 d is directly proportional to t.
  When $d = 10$, $t = 4$.
  Work out the value of d when $t = 9$.

9 If $p : q = 1 : 8$, write down a formula expressing q in terms of p.

10 $P \propto F$ and $P = 12$ when $F = 18$.
  a Write a formula in the form $P = kF$ where the value of k is to be found.
  b Find P when $F = 27$.
  c Find F when $P = 16$.

TASK M5.11   **Main Book Page 141**

1 **a** If 6 people take 5 hours to dig a trench, how long will it take 2 people to dig the same trench?
  b What assumption are you making in order to answer part **a**?

2 y is inversely proportional to x and $y = 16$ when $x = 2$.
  a Find y when $x = 10$.
  b Find x when $y = 4$.

3 In a factory 6 machines take 4 hours to pack 1920 boxes of biscuits. If 2 machines break down, how long will it take the remaining machines to pack 2880 boxes of biscuits?

4 Suzanne is doing a Science experiment. She has plotted the graph shown opposite. Does this suggest that v is inversely proportional to m? Explain your answer fully.

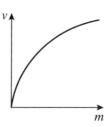

5 A is inversely proportional to B and $A = 15$ when $B = 3$.

    a Find A when $B = 9$.   **b** Find B when $A = 60$.

6 Which equations below suggest that y is inversely proportional to x?

    a $y = \frac{1}{4}x$ **b** $y = \frac{4}{x}$ **c** $xy = 6$ **d** $5y = x$ **e** $4xy = 1$

7 R is inversely proportional to I and $I = 5$ when $R = 3$.

    a Find R when $I = 7\cdot5$.   **b** Find I when $R = 30$.

8 m is inversely proportional to p^2. Write down any equation which you believe is appropriate for this relationship.

9 Find k then copy and complete the table below given that $y = \frac{k}{x}$.

x	1	4	8	
y		5		1

ALGEBRA 2   7

TASK M7.1 ———————————————————————— **Main Book Page 156**

1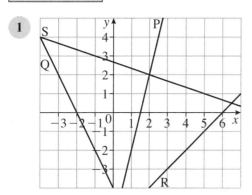

Find the gradient of each line shown opposite.

2 Copy and complete the table below then draw $y = 3x - 1$.

x	-2	-1	0	1	2
y					

3 Which two lines below are parallel?

a $y = 4x + 3$ **b** $y = 3 + 2x$ **c** $y = 1 + 4x$ **d** $y = 3x + 4$

4

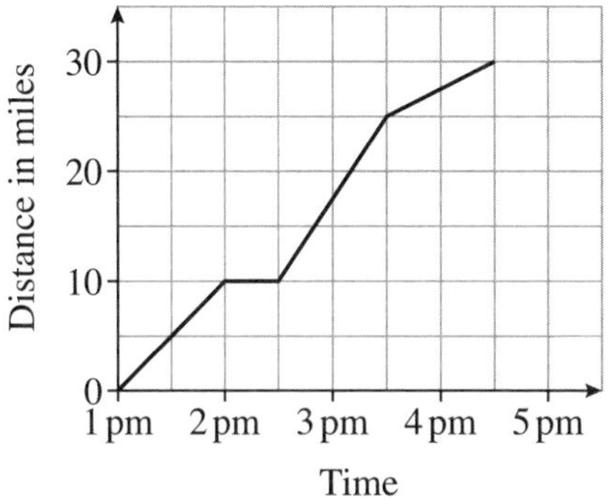

Dan cycles 30 miles as shown on the graph opposite.

a Explain what might have happened between 2 pm and 2:30 pm.

b How far had Dan cycled by 3 pm?

c Between which times was Dan's speed the greatest?

5 Draw the line $y = 2x + 2$.

6 Draw the x and y axes then any straight line with a gradient equal to -1.

7 Which line below cuts the y-axis at $(0, 5)$?

a $y = 5x + 1$ **b** $y = 4x + 5$ **c** $y = 3 + 5x$ **d** $y = 5x$

8

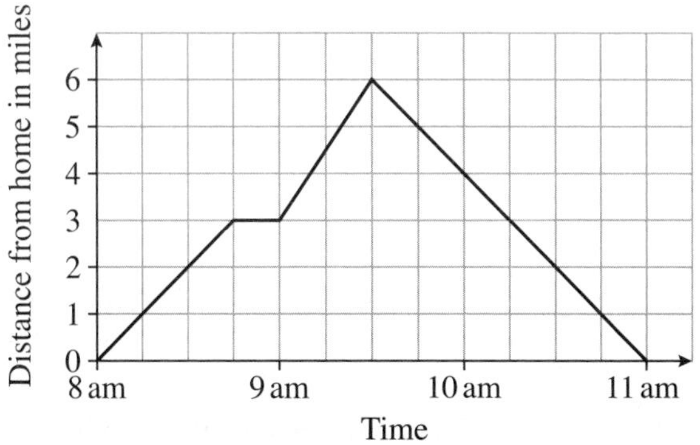

Cerys leaves her home and goes for a walk. Her journey is shown on the graph above. Describe her journey in as much detail as possible.

|

1 Expand

   a $4(x - 2)$ **b** $6(2x + 1)$ **c** $m(3m - 2n)$ **d** $n(n + 4)$

   e $3n(n - 6)$ **f** $5m(4 + m)$ **g** $n(3n + 2 - m)$ **h** $2m(n + m - 4)$

2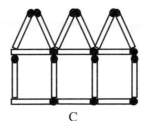

      A   B   C

A pattern of shapes made with matchsticks is shown opposite. How many matchsticks would be used in

   a shape D

   b shape E

   c shape H?

3 Make x the subject of each formula given below:

   a $y = x + 3$ **b** $v = \dfrac{x}{5}$ **c** $y = 6x - 2$ **d** $y = 4 + 2x$

   e $y = 7x$ **f** $y = \dfrac{x}{2} + 9$ **g** $4x - 3 = m$ **h** $\dfrac{x}{9} - 2 = y$

4 Solve

   a $6x + 2 = 3x + 29$ **b** $5(2x - 3) = 6x + 9$ **c** $1 = \dfrac{2x}{7} - 3$ **d** $\dfrac{6x + 5}{7} = 5$

5

A   B

n

D   C

An expression for the area of the rectangle opposite is $3n^2 + 7n$.

Write down an expression for the length of the rectangle.

6 Expand

   a $(n + 3)(n + 6)$ **b** $(y - 2)(y - 4)$ **c** $(n + 2)(n - 4)$

   d $(m - 7)(m - 3)$ **e** $(p + 2)(p + 2)$ **f** $(x - 5)^2$

7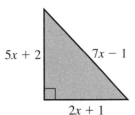

   $5x + 2$ $7x - 1$

        $2x + 1$

B   C

A $4x + 1$ D

The perimeter of the triangle opposite is 30cm. The ratio of the length to the width of the rectangle is 3 : 2.

Work out the actual width AB of the rectangle.

TASK M7.3 ──────────────────────────────── **Main Book Page 161**

> **Remember:** For an arithmetic sequence (difference between successive terms is always the same number),
>
> n^{th} term $= a + (n - 1)d$ where a is the first term in the sequence and d is the common difference between each pair of terms.

1 Match up each nth term below with its correct sequence:

A $\boxed{3n + 2}$

B $\boxed{n^2 + 1}$

C $\boxed{18 - 2n}$

1 $\boxed{2, 5, 10, 17, ...}$

2 $\boxed{5, 7, 9, 11, ...}$

3 $\boxed{5, 8, 11, 14, ...}$

4 $\boxed{16, 14, 12, 10, ...}$

2 Write down the first term and common difference for each sequence below:

   a 4, 7, 10, 13, ...   **b** 6, 11, 16, 21, ...   **c** 25, 22, 19, 16, ...

3 Work out the nth term for each arithmetic sequence in question **2**.

4 **a** Find the nth term of 8, 11, 14, 17, ...

    b Find the 30th term of 8, 11, 14, 17, ...

    c Which term of 8, 11, 14, 17, ... is equal to 80?

5 Write down the first four terms of the sequence which has an nth term equal to:

   a $n^2 + n$ **b** 3^n **c** $n(n - 3)$ **d** $\dfrac{3n - 2}{3n + 2}$

6 **a** Find the nth term of 5, 9, 13, 17, ...

    b Find the 54th term of 5, 9, 13, 17, ...

    c Which term of 5, 9, 13, 17, ... is equal to 141?

7 **a** Find the nth term of 2, 7, 12, 17, ...

    b By using the nth term of the sequence 23, 25, 27, 29, ..., find out what value of n will make the nth term of the two sequences give exactly the same value.

TASK M7.4 ———————————————————————————— Main Book Page 162

1 The *n*th term of a sequence is given by $n^2 - n$.
  a Write down the 1st term of the sequence.
  b Write down the 4th term of the sequence.
  c Write down the 10th term of the sequence.

2 Find the next 2 numbers in each sequence below:
  a 5, 8, 13, 20, 29, ...   **b** −1, 2, 7, 14, 23, ...
  c 0, 2, 6, 12, 20, ...   **d** 6, 14, 24, 36, 50, ...

3 Write down the 10th term of the sequence 2, 3, 5, 8, 13, ...

4 Here is a sequence of rectangles made from squares.
   Let *n* = shape number and *s* = number of squares

 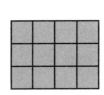 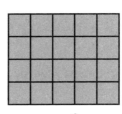 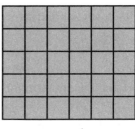

   $n = 1$ $n = 2$ $n = 3$ $n = 4$

  a Write down how many squares will be in the next shape in the sequence.
  b How many squares will be in shape number 10?

5 Write down a Fibonacci sequence.

6 Which sequences below are arithmetic and which are quadratic?
  a 3, 12, 27, 48, 75, ...   **b** 5, 11, 21, 35, 53, ...
  c 8, 15, 22, 29, 36, ...   **d** 5, 18, 37, 62, 93, ...

7 $m, n, m + n, ...$ is a Fibonacci sequence.
   Write down the next four terms of this sequence.

TASK M7.5 ─────────────────────────────── **Main Book Page 163**

> **Remember:** Geometric progression − each term is obtained by multiplying the previous term by a constant number.
> This constant number is called the common ratio, r.

1 Write down the common ratio for each geometric progression below.

a 2, 6, 18, 54, ...

b 3, −12, 48, −192, ...

c 4, $\frac{4}{3}$, $\frac{4}{9}$, $\frac{4}{27}$, ...

d 0·3, 0·06, 0·012, 0·0024, ...

2 The 5th term of a geometric progression is 48.
The 6th term is −24. Find the common ratio.

3 Find the 7th term in the geometric progression 2, 10, 50, ...

4 The 2nd term of a geometric progression is 20 and the 3rd term is 80.
Find the first term of the sequence.

5 The first two terms of a geometric progression are 4 and 12.
Find **a** the 3rd term   **b** the 5th term

6 Think of your own geometric progression and write down the first 5 terms.
Write down the common ratio.

7

$n = 1$

$n = 2$

$n = 3$

The number of triangles in the shapes opposite form a geometric progression.

a Write down the common ratio.

b How many triangles would be in the 8th shape in this sequence?

8 The 3rd term of a geometric progression is 10 and the 5th term is 160. Find the common ratio.

9 Matt invests some money and receives 5% per annum compound interest. The money at the end of each year forms a geometric progression. Write down the common ratio.

10 A sequence has nth term $= 3(4)^{n-1}$

a Write down the first 4 terms of this sequence.

b Is this sequence arithmetic, quadratic or geometric?
Give a reason for your answer.

1 Dougal rearranges $y = mx + c$ to make x the subject of the formula as shown below.

$$y = mx + c$$

$$\frac{y}{m} = x + c$$

$$\frac{y}{m} - c = x$$

so $x = \dfrac{y}{m} - c$

He has made a mistake. Explain clearly where he has made the mistake.

2 Make x the subject of each formula given below:

a $y = nx - w$ **b** $y = mx + pq$ **c** $4m + cx = n$

d $p = 2m + qx$ **e** $wx - mq = 7p$ **f** $ab + 3mx = wy$

3 Copy and fill each box below:

$$\frac{mx - 3a}{w} = y$$

$$mx - 3a = \boxed{}$$

$$mx = \boxed{} + \boxed{}$$

$$x = \frac{\boxed{} + \boxed{}}{\boxed{}}$$

4 Make x the subject of each formula given below:

a $\dfrac{wx + 5b}{3} = a$ **b** $\dfrac{wx - mn}{q} = f$ **c** $w(x + m) = p$

d $w = \dfrac{mx - ab}{5p}$ **e** $m(x - 4) = y$ **f** $9p = f(x - y)$

5 Make x the subject of the formula $m = \dfrac{ax - nw}{3p}$

1 Copy and complete:

a $\sqrt{x} + b = a$ **b** $\sqrt{(x + b)} = a$ **c** $x^3 + w = 6m$

$\sqrt{x} = a - \boxed{}$ $x + b = \boxed{}$ $x^3 = 6m - \boxed{}$

$x = (a - \boxed{})^2$ $x = \boxed{} - \boxed{}$ $x = \sqrt[\boxed{}]{(6m - \boxed{})}$

2 Make x the subject of each formula given below:

a $x^2 + b = c$ **b** $px^2 + q = r$ **c** $ax^2 = b$

d $\dfrac{ax^2}{b} = c$ **e** $\sqrt{x} - m = w$ **f** $\dfrac{\sqrt{x} + u}{v} = z$

g $\dfrac{a\sqrt{x} + b}{c} = d$ **h** $a - x^3 = b$ **i** $\dfrac{\sqrt{(x - p)}}{t} = r$

3 $v^2 = u^2 + 2as$ Make u the subject of the formula.

4 $A = 4\pi r^3$ Make r the subject of the formula.

5 $w = up + 4aq^2$ Make a the subject of the formula.

6 $A = 8(w - p)^2$ Make w the subject of the formula.

7 Make n the subject of each formula given below:

a $h = \dfrac{m}{n}$ **b** $\dfrac{n}{v} - x = w$ **c** $h - \dfrac{n}{g} = k$

8 $\dfrac{h + a}{b} = \dfrac{x + d}{c}$ Make x the subject of the formula.

9 $T = \sqrt{\left(\dfrac{w - a}{g}\right)}$ Make w the subject of the formula.

10 Make y the subject of each formula given below:

a $\sqrt{\left(\dfrac{y}{m}\right)} = h$ **b** $\sqrt[3]{(y - z)} = r$ **c** $A = \dfrac{1}{2}my^3$

d $\sqrt[3]{(ay - b)} = c$ **e** $\sqrt{(my + n)} = p$ **f** $v - y^3 = a$

g $py^3 - q = x$ **h** $\sqrt{\left(\dfrac{y - m}{n}\right)} = w$ **i** $x = \dfrac{\sqrt[3]{(my + p)}}{3}$

TASK E7.2   **Main Book Page 168**

Remember: $mx + yx = w$ Make x the subject.

x is in two terms so take out as a common factor

$x(m + y) = w$

$$\dfrac{x\cancel{(m + y)}}{\cancel{m + y}} = \dfrac{w}{m + y}$$

$$x = \dfrac{w}{m + y}$$

1 Copy and complete:

a $ax - b = cx$

$ax - cx = \boxed{}$

$x(\boxed{} - \boxed{}) = \boxed{}$

$x = \dfrac{\boxed{}}{\boxed{} - \boxed{}}$

b $\dfrac{v + 3w}{v} = p$

$v + 3w = \boxed{}$

$3w = \boxed{} - \boxed{}$

$3w = v(\boxed{} - \boxed{})$

$v = \dfrac{3w}{\boxed{} - \boxed{}}$

2 Make x the subject of each formula given below:

a $cx + f = mx$

b $mx - w = px$

c $ax + b = cx + d$

d $a(x - c) = b(x + f)$

e $4x = m(x + y)$

f $p + qx = m(n - x)$

3 Make x the subject of the formula $\qquad a = \dfrac{c + bx}{x}$

4 Make m the subject of the formula $\qquad m = \dfrac{d + em}{a}$

5 Make w the subject of the formula $\qquad \dfrac{w + b}{aw} = c$

6 Make q the subject of the formula $\qquad \dfrac{kq}{q + b} = e$

7 Make n the subject of each formula given below:

a $\dfrac{a - bn}{n} = c$

b $\dfrac{n - c}{n} = a$

c $\dfrac{n}{n + a} = b$

8 $\dfrac{aw + y}{c} = \dfrac{bw + u}{d}$ Make w the subject of the formula.

TASK M7.7 ———————————————————— **Main Book Page 170**

> **Reminder:** $\neq$ means 'not equal to'

1 Copy and fill each box below with $<$ or $>$.

a $15 \boxed{} 19$

b $2{\cdot}4 \boxed{} 1{\cdot}4$

c $302 \boxed{} 299$

d $-3 \boxed{} -4$

2 Answer true or false:

a $3{\cdot}09 > 3{\cdot}1$

b $0{\cdot}2 \neq \dfrac{1}{5}$

c $-8 < -4$

d $3\dfrac{1}{4} > 3{\cdot}5$

e $30\% \neq 0{\cdot}3$

f $6{\cdot}81 > 6{\cdot}59$

g $\dfrac{1}{4} < 0{\cdot}3$

h $\dfrac{3}{25} \neq 9\%$

3 If $n \leqslant 4\cdot 5$, which of the values for n below would be allowed?

4

Write down the inequalities shown below:

a

6

b

−3

c

−1

d

2   6

e

−2   3

f

−4   0

5 Draw a number line to show the following inequalities.

a $x \geqslant 1$ **b** $x < -6$ **c** $4 \leqslant x \leqslant 9$
d $-2 < x < 0$ **e** $-3 \leqslant x < 2$ **f** $-5 < x \leqslant -1$

6 $n < 5$ and $n \geqslant -1$. Show this on a number line.

TASK M7.8 ——————————————————— **Main Book Page 171**

Solve the inequalities below:

1 $x + 6 > 12$ **2** $x + 3 < -2$ **3** $x - 4 \leqslant 7$

4 $x - 6 < 0$ **5** $4x \geqslant 12$ **6** $\dfrac{x}{2} > 9$

7 $3x + 2 > 17$ **8** $4x - 8 \leqslant 12$ **9** $2(x + 3) < 18$

10 $6(x - 2) \geqslant 24$ **11** $6x - 4 > 3x + 17$ **12** $\dfrac{x}{4} - 3 \leqslant 3$

13 Write down the largest *integer x* for which $2x < 7$.

14 Write down the largest *integer x* for which $5x < 12$.

15 Write down all the *integer values* (*whole numbers*) of x which satisfy each inequality below.

a $4 \leqslant x \leqslant 7$ **b** $0 < x \leqslant 5$ **c** $-2 < x < 0$
d $-3 \leqslant x \leqslant 3$ **e** $-4 \leqslant x < -1$ **f** $-6 < x < 1$

16 In each case below, find the range of values of x which satisfy both the inequalities and show this answer on a number line.

    a $x + 5 < 7$ and $x - 2 \geqslant -3$

    b $2x + 1 > -5$ and $3(2x + 1) < 21$

    c $\dfrac{x - 5}{2} \leqslant 3$ and $4x - 7 \geqslant 13$

17 Esther has £n. Paul has four times as much money as Esther. Misha has £10 more than Paul.
The sum of their money is at least £55 but no more than £82.
Work out how much money, £n, Esther might have.

TASK M7.9 ————————————————————————— **Main Book Page 173**

Copy and complete

1 $x^2 - 3x - 18 = 0$

    $(x - 6)(x + \square) = 0$

    $x - 6 = 0$ or $x + \square = 0$

    $x = \square$ or $x = \square$

2 $n^2 + 3n = 0$

    $n(\square + \square) = 0$

    $n = 0$ or $\square + \square = 0$

    $n = 0$ or $n = \square$

3 $a^2 - 4a = 5$

    $a^2 - 4a - \square = 0$

    $(a + 1)(a - \square) = 0$

    $a + 1 = 0$ or $a - \square = 0$

    $a = \square$ or $a = \square$

Solve these equations

4 $x^2 - 3x + 2 = 0$

5 $a^2 + 4a + 3 = 0$

6 $m^2 + 7m + 10 = 0$

7 $y^2 + y - 12 = 0$

8 $n^2 + 3n - 10 = 0$

9 $x^2 - 8x + 12 = 0$

10 $c^2 + 2c - 15 = 0$

11 $(m - 6)(m + 4) = 0$

12 $(a - 3)(a - 7) = 0$

13 $n^2 - 5n = 0$

14 $x^2 + 7x = 0$

15 $y^2 - 6y = 0$

Rearrange to make each equation $= 0$ then solve.

16 $p^2 + 5p = 14$

17 $n^2 + 32 = 12n$

18 $b^2 - 3b = 0$

19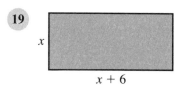

The area of this rectangle is $91\,\text{cm}^2$.
Form an equation involving x then solve
it to find the value of x.

20 $s = ut + \dfrac{1}{2}at^2$ is a formula used in Science where t is time. Find the values of t if
$s = -12$, $u = -7$ and $a = 2$.

1 Use the graph opposite to find the roots of
$$x^2 + 5x + 1 = 0$$
Give your answers to one decimal place.

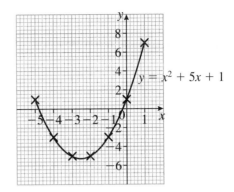

2 Use the graph opposite to find the roots of
a $x^2 - 3x - 2 = 0$
b $x^2 - 3x - 2 = 1$
c $x^2 - 3x - 2 = -3$

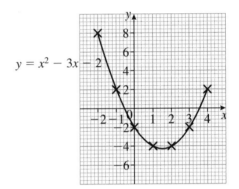

3 **a** Draw the graph of $y = x^2 - 2x$
for x-values from -2 to 4.

Use the graph to find the roots
(to one decimal place) of:

b $x^2 - 2x = 0$
c $x^2 - 2x = 1$
d $x^2 - 2x = 4$

1 **a** Draw these axes.
b If $3x + y = 6$, find the value of y when $x = 0$.
c If $3x + y = 6$, find the value of x when $y = 0$.
d Plot 2 points from *b* and *c* and join them up
to make the straight line $3x + y = 6$.

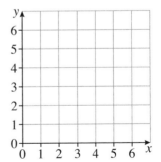

2 Draw each line below with the 'cover-up' method.
You need to find the 2 points first then draw the
axes big enough.

a $2x + 3y = 12$ **b** $3x + 7y = 21$
c $8x + 5y = 40$ **d** $4x - 3y = 24$

3 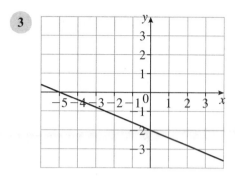 The line $2x + 5y = -10$ is drawn opposite using the 'cover-up' method. Is the line in the correct position? Explain the reasons for your answer.

TASK M7.12 ──────────────────────────────── **Main Book Page 178**

1 Use the graph to solve the simultaneous equations below:

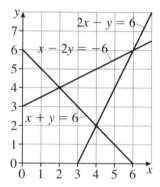

a $x + y = 6$
   $2x - y = 6$

b $x - 2y = -6$
   $2x - y = 6$

c $x + y = 6$
   $x - 2y = -6$

2 **a** Draw an x-axis from 0 to 7.
   Draw a y-axis from -5 to 5.

   b Use the cover up method to draw the line $2x + 3y = 12$.

   c Use the cover up method to draw the line $4x - 2y = 8$.

   d Use your graph to solve the simultaneous equations $2x + 3y = 12$
                                                           $4x - 2y = 8$

3 By drawing graphs, solve the following pairs of simultaneous equations:

   a $x + y = 4$ **b** $5x + 2y = 20$ **c** $2x + y = 7$
      $y = x + 2$ $x - 2y = -8$ $y = 2x - 5$

TASK M7.13 ──────────────────────────────── **Main Book Page 180**

1 Add together the simultaneous equations: $3x + 2y = 7$
                                          and $7x - 2y = 3$

   Use your answer to find the value of x.

   Use your answer to find the value of y.

Solve the simultaneous equations

2 $2x + 3y = 12$
    $5x + 3y = 21$

3 $4x + y = 13$
    $4x + 3y = 23$

4 $3x + y = 16$
    $2x - y = 9$

5 $4x - 3y = 0$
$7x + 3y = 33$

6 $5x + 4y = 24$
$3x - 4y = -24$

7 $2x - 5y = -12$
$3x - 5y = -13$

8 $4x + 2y = 10$
$7x - 2y = 34$

9 $3x + 5y = -11$
$3x - 4y = -2$

10 $2x - 2y = -16$
$3x - 2y = -21$

TASK M7.14 | **Main Book Page 181**

Solve the simultaneous equations:

1 $3x + 4y = 17$
$6x + y = 20$

2 $2a + 3b = 14$
$3a + 2b = 11$

3 $4m + 3n = 26$
$3m - 5n = -24$

4 $5c - 4d = 21$
$2c - 3d = 7$

5 $2p - 3q = -11$
$p + 4q = 11$

6 $7a + 3b = 22$
$5a - 2b = 24$

7 $3m + 4n = 11$
$2m + 6n = 9$

8 $4x - 3y = 2$
$5x + 7y = -19$

9 $10x - 3y = -14$
$4x - 5y = -17$

10 Solve the simultaneous equations $3x + 2y = 5$
$6x + 4y = 8$

Explain what happens. What might this mean if you draw both lines on a graph?

TASK E7.4 | **Main Book Page 182**

Answer these questions by forming a pair of simultaneous equations then solving them.

1 Darren buys 3 pairs of socks and 2 pairs of underpants for £25. Colin buys 2 pairs of socks and 7 pairs of underpants for £62. What is the cost of a pair of socks and a pair of underpants.

2 The sum of two numbers is 19. The difference between four times one number and the other number is 41. Find the values of the two numbers.

3 Howlton primary school buy 10 solar calculators and 30 battery calculators for £210. Merryfield primary school buy 15 solar calculators and 8 battery calculators for £130. Find the cost of one solar calculator and one battery calculator.

4 Penny buys 5 adult tickets and 3 child tickets for the theatre. The tickets cost her a total of £164. Barney buys 4 adult tickets and 4 child tickets at a total cost of £152. Find the cost of one adult ticket and one child ticket.

5

Triangle ABC is isosceles.

Work out the actual length of AB.
All lengths are in cm.

6 A straight line passes through the points (2, 11) and (−1, 2).
The equation of a straight line is $y = mx + c$. Find the values of m and c.

7 A bookstall is selling all its hard backs at the same price and all its paper backs at the same price. A woman buys 7 hard backs and 5 paper backs for £61·40. A man buys 11 hard backs and 7 paper backs for £93·10. Find the price of one hard back and one paper back.

8 Charlie has four times as many sweets as Anna. Charlie eats 14 sweets and Anna eats 2 sweets. If Charlie now has three times as many sweets as Anna, how many sweets have Charlie and Anna each got *now*?

TASK M7.15 ———————————————————————— **Main Book Page 183**

1 **a** Copy and complete the table below then draw the curve $y = x^2 + 2$

x	−3	−2	−1	0	1	2	3
y							

b Write down the co-ordinates of the turning point (vertex).

2 **a** Copy and complete the table below then draw the curve $y = x^2 + 4x$.

x	−5	−4	−3	−2	−1	0	1	2
x^2				4				4
$+4x$				−8				8
y				−4				12

b Write down the co-ordinates of
  i the turning point, **ii** the y-intercept and **iii** the intercepts with the x-axis.

3 Repeat question **2** for the curve $y = x^2 + 5x − 4$

1 **a** Copy and complete the table opposite then draw the curve $y = x^3 - 2x + 1$.
  b Write down the co-ordinates of the y-intercept.
  c Write down the co-ordinates of the turning points.

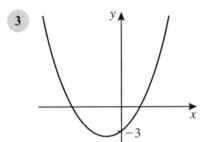

x	-3	-2	-1	0	1	2	3
x^3		-8					
$-2x$		$+4$					
$+1$	$+1$	$+1$					
y		-3					

2 **a** Draw the graph of $y = x^3 - 2x^2 + 3$ for x-values from -2 to 4.
  b Write down the co-ordinates of the y-intercept.
  c Write down the co-ordinates of the turning points.

3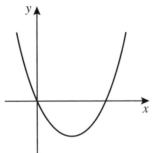

Martin suggests that the equation of the curve opposite is $y = 5x - 3$.

Explain clearly why he cannot be correct.

4

1.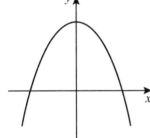

2.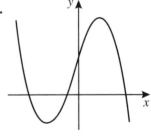

3.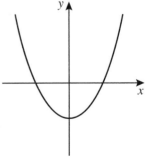

4.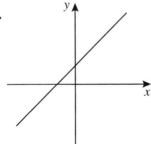

5.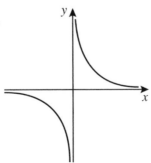

6.

Match each equation to its graph above. One of the equations does not have a graph above.

A $y = \dfrac{5}{x}$ **B** $y = x^2 - 10$ **C** $y = x^2 - x$ **D** $y = 1 - 4x$

E $y = 6 - x^2$ **F** $y = 5 + 7x - x^3$ **G** $y = 4x + 1$

5 **a** Draw the graph of $y = \dfrac{20}{x-1}$ for x-values from -4 to 6 (be careful when $x = 1$).

   b Use the graph to estimate the x-value when $y = -8$.

TASK M7.16   **Main Book Page 188**

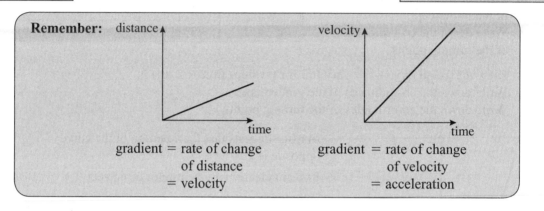

Remember:

distance
gradient = rate of change
of distance
= velocity

velocity
gradient = rate of change
of velocity
= acceleration

1

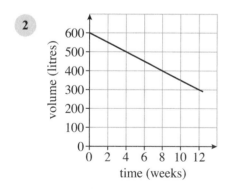

time (minutes)

A swimming pool is being filled with water. The volume of the water in the pool is shown in the graph opposite. Work out the rate of change of the volume of water in m^3 per minute.

2

volume (litres)

time (weeks)

The graph shows the amount of oil in a house oil tank. Work out the rate of decrease of the oil in litres per week.

3 s is the distance (in km) from a factory. A lorry travels such that $s = 40t$ where t is the time (in hours).

   a Draw a graph of s against t for t-values from 0 to 3.

   b Work out the lorry's speed.

4 The velocity–time graph opposite shows the motion of a train. Find

   a the acceleration between $t = 0$ and $t = 20$

   b the deceleration between $t = 50$ and $t = 90$

   c the acceleration between $t = 20$ and $t = 50$

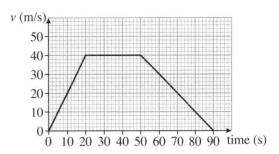

5

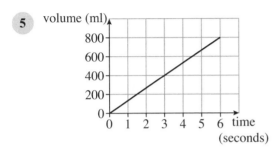

Some cider is being poured into a bottle.
The graph shows the volume of cider in the bottle.

Work out the rate of change of the volume of cider in millilitres per second.

6

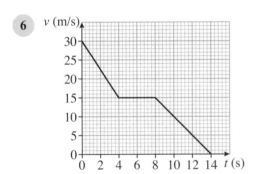

The velocity–time graph opposite shows the motion of a particle. Find

   a the deceleration between $t = 0$ and $t = 4$

   b the velocity between $t = 4$ and $t = 8$

   c the deceleration between $t = 8$ and $t = 14$

TASK M7.17   **Main Book Page 191**

1 Which of the following lines pass through the point $(0, -2)$?

   a $y = -2x + 3$ **b** $y = 6 - 2x$ **c** $y = 6x - 2$

   d $y = x - 2$ **e** $y = -2x$ **f** $y = -2 + 2x$

2 Write down the equation of any line parallel to $y = 4x - 1$.

3 Work out the gradient of each line below.

   a $y = \frac{1}{3}x + 2$ **b** $y = 3 + 4x$ **c** $y - x = 2$ **d** $4x - y = 1$

4 Find the y-intercept of each line below.

   a $y = 2x - 4$ **b** $y = \frac{1}{3} + 5x$ **c** $y - 3x = 4$ **d** $6x + y = -1$

5 Is $4x - y = 2$ parallel to $y = 3 + 4x$? Explain your answer fully.

6 Sam says that the line $2x + 4y = 8$ meets the line $y = -3x + 2$ at the point $(0, 2)$. Hannah does not agree. Show clearly who is correct.

7 Is $2x + y = 5$ parallel to $4x + 4y = 8$? Explain your answer fully.

8 Consider $y = 2x + 3$.

The line cuts the y-axis at $(0, 3)$.

The gradient is 2 so the line goes up 2 units for every 1 unit across.

This information can be used to sketch the line shown opposite.

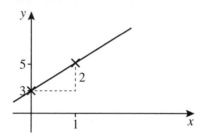

Use your knowledge of $y = mx + c$ to sketch each of the following lines:

a $y = 4x + 1$ **b** $y = 3x - 2$ **c** $y = 4 - 3x$

| **TASK E7.6** | **Main Book Page 192** |

1 Find the equation of the straight line which passes through $(0, 5)$ and has a gradient of 6.

2 Find the equation of the straight line which passes through $(1, 5)$ and has a gradient of 2.

3 Find the equation of the straight line which passes through $(-2, 4)$ and has a gradient of 3.

4 Write down the equation of each line shown below:

a

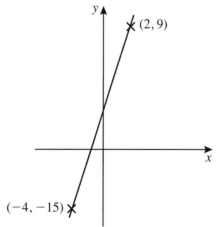

b

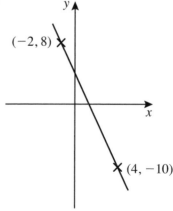

5 Find the equation of the straight line which passes through $(-6, 12)$ and $(2, 8)$.

6 Find the equation of the line that is parallel to the line $y = 5x + 3$ and passes through $(1, 6)$.

7 Find the equation of the straight line which passes through $(2, 4)$ and $(5, 10)$.

8 Find the equation of the line that is parallel to the line $y = 3x - 2$ and passes through $(6, 5)$.

9 Find the equation of the straight line which passes through $(1, 6)$ and $(4, -6)$.

10

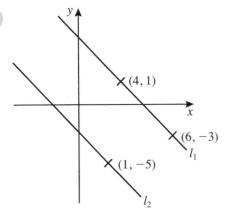

Find the equation of line l_2 opposite if line l_2 is parallel to line l_1.

STATISTICS 1   8

| **TASK M8.1** | **Main Book Page 201** |

1 There are 16 yellow balls and 24 green balls in a box. All the remaining balls in the box are pink. The probability of randomly removing a pink ball is $\frac{1}{5}$. How many pink balls are in the box?

2 The probability of turning up early for a meal is $\frac{1}{5}$ and the probability of turning up late for a meal is $\frac{1}{3}$. What is the probability of being on time for a meal?

3 Mary keeps throwing a drawing pin to find out how many times it will land 'point down'. The table below shows the total number of times the drawing pin has landed 'point down' after every 20 throws.

Number of throws	20	40	60	80	100	120	140	160	180	200
Number of 'point down'	5	13	21	26	36	47	53	59	68	76

   a Work out the relative frequency of the drawing pin landing 'point down' after every 20 throws (round off to 2 decimal places if necessary).

   b Plot a graph of the relative frequency of 'point down' against the total number of throws.

   c Write down the number around which the relative frequency of 'point down' is settling.

   d If the drawing pin is thrown 600 times, how many times would you expect it to land 'point down'?

4 Reuben throws an 8-sided dice (faces numbered from 1 to 8) once.
What is the probability of getting:

a a multiple of 2   **b** a prime number   **c** a factor of 8

5 Each week Darryl plays Simon at squash. The probability of Darryl losing is 0·3.
The probability of Darryl winning is equal to the probability of Darryl drawing.

	Win	Draw	Lose
Probability	x	x	0·3

a What is the probability of Darryl winning?

b How many times would Darryl expect to lose during 20 weeks?

6 One night a kennel has 16 dogs and 7 cats in its care. The following morning 3 dogs and 4 cats
are picked up by their owners and 2 dogs are dropped off at the kennel.

Another owner arrives. What is the probability that if the owner has come to pick up one pet
only, it will be a cat?

TASK M8.2 ──────────────────────────── **Main Book Page 203**

1

Marie and Don play a
game involving a spinner
and a dice.

Marie wins if the spinner gives a square number and the dice gives a multiple of 3.

Don wins if the spinner gives an even number and the dice gives a factor of 15.

Any other outcome is a draw.

Is this game fair to both players? Give reasons for your answer.

2 The frequency tree shows a group of 100 people and whether they are 65 years old or over and
whether they drive.

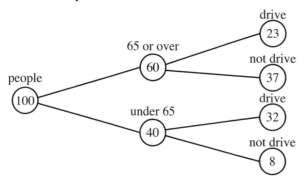

What is the probability that a person
chosen at random drives?

3 Five people throw a biased dice several times.
They record how many times the dice lands on a '2'.

Name	Number of throws	Number of 2's	Relative frequency
Helena	100	41	0·41
Sandeep	200	83	0·415
Rory	150	60	0·4
Natalie	450	99	0·22
Ben	700	273	0·39

One of these five people made a mistake when recording the number of 2's.
Who do you think this was? Give a reason for your answer.

4 The king, queen and jack of hearts and diamonds are removed from a pack of 52 playing cards.
One card is removed at random from the remaining cards. What is the probability of getting:

a a king   **b** a red card   **c** an ace?

5 The information in the Venn diagram below describes 150 people at an Education show.
T = {teachers} and B = {people with beards}.

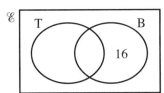

There are 6 teachers with beards and 53 people who are not teachers and do not have beards.

If one person is chosen at random then find

a the probability that the person is a teacher who does not have a beard.

b the probability that the person does not have a beard.

6 Assume there is an even chance for Chelsea giving birth to a boy or a girl.

a Find the probability of Chelsea giving birth to 3 girls.

b Find the probability of Chelsea giving birth to one boy and two girls.

7 The table below shows the results one season for Arsenal and Liverpool.

	Won	Drawn	Lost
Arsenal	22	10	6
Liverpool	19	12	7

a If one of Liverpool's matches is chosen at random, what is the probability that Liverpool won the match?

b If a match is chosen for either team, what is the probability that the match was a draw?

82

8 Every Saturday morning, Jay either walks, gardens or shops. The probabilities of Jay doing each activity is shown below.

Activity	Walk	Garden	Shop
Probability	n	$\frac{1}{4}$	$\frac{3}{10}$

a What is the probability of Jay going for a walk?

b How many times will Jay go shopping during the first 50 Saturdays of the year?

9 120 people work for a firm. Two-thirds of them work in the factory and the rest work in the office. 35% of the factory workers are female and 80% of the office workers are female.

a Copy and complete the frequency tree.

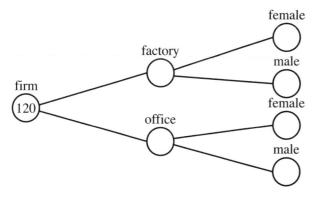

b If a person working for the firm is chosen at random, what is the probability that this person is male?

10 Tina has n playing cards of which 6 are red.

If a card is taken at random from Tina, what is the probability that it is a black card?

| **TASK M8.3** | **Main Book Page 207** |

1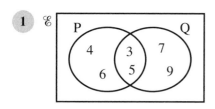

Find

a Q' **b** $P \cap Q$ **c** $n(P)$

d $P \cup Q'$ **e** $P' \cup Q'$ **f** $P' \cap Q$

2 $A = \{4, 5, 8, 9, 10\}$, $B = \{5, 9, 11, 12\}$ and $C = \{2, 3, 5, 9, 10, 11\}$.

Find

a $B \cup C$ **b** $n(A \cap B)$ **c** $(A \cap B) \cup C$ **d** $A \cap B \cap C$

3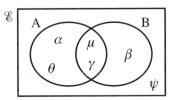

Find

a $(A \cup B)'$ **b** $A \cap B'$ **c** $n(A' \cap B)$

d $n(B')$ **e** $(A \cup B')'$ **f** $(A \cap B')'$

4 $M = \{x : x$ is a prime number, $5 < x \leq 12\}$ and $N = \{10, 11, 12, 13, 14\}$.

State which of the statements below are true?

a $M \cap N = \{11\}$ **b** $n(M \cup N) = 7$ **c** $7 \in M \cup N$

5 Find

a $A' \cup B$ **b** $n(A' \cap B)$ **c** A'

d $(A \cup B)'$ **e** $A \cup B'$ **f** $(A' \cap B)'$

g $n(A' \cup B)'$ **h** $(A \cup B')'$ **i** $(A' \cap B')'$

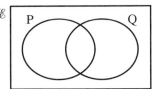

TASK M8.4 ——————————————————— **Main Book Page 208**

1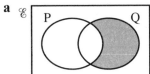

Draw 6 diagrams like the one shown opposite.

Shade each of the following sets.

a $(P \cup Q)'$ **b** $P' \cap Q$ **c** P'

d $(P \cap Q)'$ **e** $P \cup Q'$ **f** $(P' \cup Q)'$

2 Describe each shaded region.

a 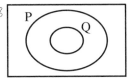 **b** 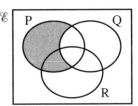 **c**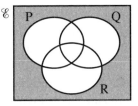

3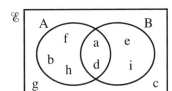

Copy the diagram opposite and shade $P' \cup Q$.

4 Draw 6 diagrams like the one shown opposite.
Shade each of the following sets.

a $P \cup Q'$ **b** $P \cap (Q \cup R)$ **c** $(P \cap Q') \cap R$

d $(P \cap R) \cup Q'$ **e** $P' \cap (Q' \cap R)$ **f** $(P \cap Q \cap R')'$

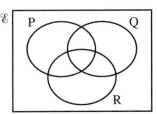

TASK M8.5 ──────────────────────────── **Main Book Page 209**

1 The Venn diagram shows

   ℰ = {people on a flight to Austria}

   H = {people from Hatton}

   S = {people going to ski}

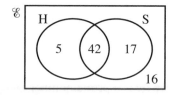

If one person is chosen at random then find

a p (person from Hatton)　　　　　　**b** p (person who skis)

c p (person from Hatton who does not ski)　　**d** p (person does not ski)

2 The Venn diagram shows

   ℰ = {Year 11 students in Horton High School}

   B = {Year 11 students who eat a school breakfast}

   L = {Year 11 students who eat a school lunch}

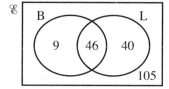

a Find p (B ∪ L).

b Find p (B′ ∩ L).

c Describe in words what p (B′ ∩ L) means.

d Find p (a student eats a school breakfast or school lunch but not both).

e Find p (B ∪ L′).

3 If $p(A ∩ B') = p(A ∩ B)$, find the value of p (B′).

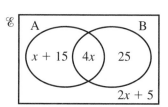

4 83 cars are examined for power steering (P), air conditioning (C) and automatic windows (W). 16 cars have power steering only, 10 have air conditioning only and 6 have automatic windows only, 5 cars have P, C and W.

16 cars have P and W (no C), x cars have C and W (no P) and $2x$ cars have P and C (no W). The same number of cars have no P, C or W as have P and C (no W).

If one car is chosen at random, find

a p (P)　　　　**b** p (C ∩ W)　　　　**c** p (C ∪ W)　　　　**d** p (C ∩ P′)

e How many cars have no P, C or W?

5 75 people attend a Music course. 28 of them play the piano and 40 of them play the guitar. 11 of them play both the piano and the guitar. If one of these people is chosen at random, find the probability that this person does not play piano or the guitar.

TASK M8.6 ──────────────────────────────── **Main Book Page 211**

1 A coin is thrown twice. What is the probability of getting 2 heads?

2 A dice is thrown twice. What is the probability of getting a '3' *followed* by a '4'?

3 A card is taken from a pack of 52 playing cards then replaced. Another card is chosen. What is the probability of obtaining:

   a 2 diamond cards?

   b 2 aces?

4 A bag contains 6 yellow beads, 3 blue beads and 2 green beads. I remove one bead at random, replace it then take another bead.

   What is the probability that:

   a both beads are blue?

   b both beads are green?

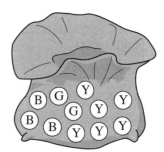

5 The probability that Will takes an umbrella to work is 0·4.

   The probability that it rains is 0·7.

   What is the probability that:

   a Will takes his umbrella and it rains?

   b Will does *not* take his umbrella and it rains?

   c Will does *not* take his umbrella and it does *not* rain?

6 2 darts are thrown at this board.

   Assuming each dart hits the board, what is the probability that:

   a both darts hit an even number?

   b both darts hit a square number?

   c both darts hit a prime number?

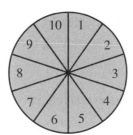

7 If a dice is thrown four times, what is the probability of obtaining four sixes?

8 The probability that Serena works on a Saturday is $\frac{3}{4}$. The probability that she goes to a night club on a Saturday evening is $\frac{4}{7}$.

   On any Saturday what is the probability that:

   a Serena does *not* work but goes to a night club?

   b Serena works and goes to a night club?

9 A bag contains 10 red and white balls. There are n red balls. Write down an expression, in terms of n, for the probability of removing a red ball followed by a white ball if I remove two balls randomly.

TASK M8.7 ──────────────────────────── **Main Book Page 213**

1 The players in an amateur football team have the jobs shown below:

Team position	Job
goalkeeper	plumber
defenders	teacher, farmer, mechanic, artist
midfielders	farmer, fireman, insurance salesman
forwards	electrician, teacher, bus driver

Which of the following pairs are mutually exclusive?

a a teacher and a midfielder

b a farmer and a defender

c an electrician and a forward

2 The probability of Karen playing certain sports is shown in the table below.

Hockey	Football	Badminton	Netball
0·5	0·1	x	0·2

a What is the probability of Karen playing hockey or netball?

b What is the probability of Karen playing badminton?

3 The probability of the next person walking into the room being a woman is $\frac{1}{3}$.

The probability of the next person walking into the room wearing glasses is $\frac{1}{10}$.

The probability of the next person walking into the room being a woman wearing glasses is $\frac{1}{30}$.

Work out the probability of the next person walking into the room being a woman or wearing glasses.

4 A bag contains 6 blue beads numbered 1 to 6. It also contains 6 yellow beads numbered 1 to 6. If one bead is randomly removed, what is the probability of taking a blue bead or a bead with the number 6 on it?

5 Dan gets to work by either car, bus, tube or bike. The table shows the probability of each being used.

Car	Bus	Tube	Bike
0·25		0·4	0·2

   a What is the probability of Dan going to work by bus?

   b What is the probability of Dan going to work by car or bus?

   c On his 20 working days in March, how many days would you expect Dan to take the take the tube?

6 There are 4 people in a car. One person is wearing glasses. 2 people are wearing hats.
Explain why the probability of a person in the car wearing glasses or a hat is *not* necessarily $\frac{3}{4}$.

7 John has some coins in his pocket. He has £1, £2 and 50p coins.
The probability of choosing a £1 coin is 0·65. The probability of choosing a £2 coin is 0·2.

   a What is the probability of choosing a 50p coin?

   b What is the probability of choosing a £2 coin or a 50p coin?

8 A dartboard has 20 sectors. Half the sectors are red and half are yellow. The red sectors have the odd numbers 1 to 19 and the yellow sectors have the even numbers 2 to 20.

A dart can land randomly on any sector. What is the probability that the dart will land on a yellow sector or a sector with a multiple of 3?

TASK M8.8 ———————————————————————— **Main Book Page 215**

1 A bag contains 8 blue discs and 3 green discs.
One disc is removed at random then replaced.
Another disc is then removed.

   a Copy and complete the tree diagram to show all the outcomes.

Find the probability that:

   b both discs are blue

   c both discs are green

   d one disc is blue and one disc is green (in any order)

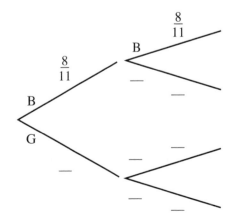

2 The probability of Jack swimming on any one day is 0·3.

   a Copy and complete the tree diagram showing whether he swims or not on a Thursday and Friday.

   b Find the probability that:

      i Jack does *not* swim on either day

      ii Jack swims on one day *only*

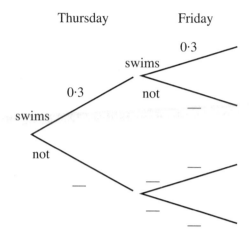

3 A spinner is spun three times.

   a Copy and complete the tree diagram to show the probability of getting a 'two'.

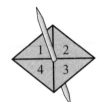

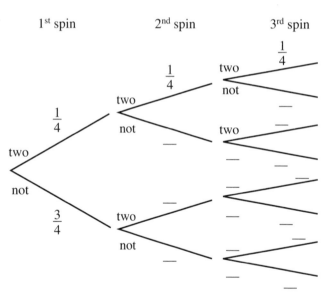

   b Find the probability that the spinner lands on:

      i 3 two's

      ii no two's

      iii at *least* one 'two'

4 A dice is thrown three times. Find the probability that the dice lands on:

   a exactly two 3's

   b *at least* one 3

5 The probability of Stacey eating a curry on any day is 0·2.
Draw a tree diagram to help you find the probability that on a Friday.
Saturday and Sunday:

a Stacey has a curry each day

b Stacey has a curry on exactly one day only

c Stacey has a curry on *at least* one day

TASK M8.9 ——————————————————————— **Main Book Page 219**

1 There are 3 males and 5 females in a family
of 8 people. Two of the family members
are chosen at random.

a Copy and complete the tree diagram.

Find the probability that:

b both people are female

c exactly one person is female

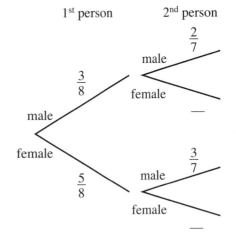

2 Charlie has 7 creme eggs and 2 caramel eggs. He eats 2 eggs randomly.

a Draw a tree diagram to show all outcomes.

Find the probability that:

b Charlie eats 2 creme eggs

c Charlie eats one creme egg and one caramel egg

d Charlie eats 2 eggs of the same type

3 Three cards are taken at random from
a pack of 52 cards.

a Copy and complete the tree diagram.

b Find the probability that:

   i all 3 cards are clubs

   ii *at least* one card is a club

   iii exactly one card is a club

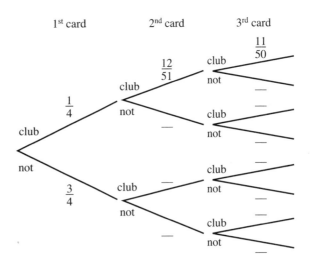

4 There are 12 beads in a bag. 5 beads are red and the rest are blue.
Three beads are taken out at random, one at a time, without replacement.

a Draw a tree diagram to show all outcomes.

Find the probability that:

b all three beads are blue

c *at least* one bead is red

d exactly one bead is blue and two beads are red

5 A box contains 15 counters. *x* counters are red and the remainder are blue. Two counters are removed at random. What is the probability, in terms of *x*, of removing:

a two blue counters?

b one counter of each colour?

| **TASK M8.10** | **Main Book Page 221** |

1 The Venn diagram opposite gives information about 80 butterflies which are observed.

R = {butterflies with red wings}

B = {butterflies with black spots on their wings}

$\mathcal{E}$ R B
21 9 16
34

Work out

a $p(R \cap B)$ **b** $p(R')$ **c** $p(R' \cap B)$ **d** $p(B \cup R')$

2 The probability of a garden gate being left open is 0.15.
If the gate is left open, the probability of a dog getting out of the garden is 0.8.
If the gate is shut, the probability of a dog getting out of the garden is 0.3.

a Copy and complete the tree diagram.

b Find the probability that the dog gets out of the garden.

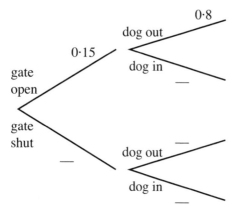

3 The frequency tree shows 160 washing machines and whether they are 3 years old or more and whether they develop a fault during the current year.

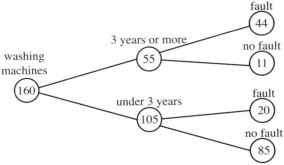

a Find the probability that a washing machine chosen at random has developed a fault during the current year.

b Given that a washing machine is 3 years old or more, what is the probability that it has not developed a fault during the current year?

4 A rugby team plays 40% of its matches at home. They win 75% of their home matches but only 55% of their away matches.

a Draw a tree diagram to represent the above information.

b Find the probability that the team wins a match.

5 Some people are asked whether during one week they had a pizza (P), an indian meal (I) or a chinese meal (C).

7 people said they had all 3.
8 people said they had P and I (no C).
12 people said they had I and C (no P).
14 people said they had P and C (no I).
16 people said they had P only.
25 people said they had I only.
23 people said they had C only.
42 people had none of this food.
One person is selected at random. Find

a $p(I)$ **b** $p(C \cap P)$

c $p(I \cap C')$ **d** $p(I \cap P \cap C)$

e Describe in words exactly what is meant by $p(I \cap C')$.

6 $\mathscr{E}$

G		H
$3x - 2y$	x	$2x + y$
	$x + 2y$	

The Venn diagram shows how many students in a school study Geography (G) or History (H) in Year 11 in Hatton High School.

There are 88 students in total. The same number of students study Geography only as study History only.

If one student is chosen at random, find the probability that the student studies Geography and History.

GEOMETRY 2   9

TASK M9.1 ───────────────────────────── **Main Book Page 231**

1 Jack and Alice go to the cinema together but watch different films. Jack's film starts at 19:50 and last for 2 hours 24 minutes.

Alice's film starts at 20:05 and lasts for 2 hours 32 minutes.

How long must Jack wait for Alice after his film has ended?

2 How much must be added to 17 932 kg to make 20 tonnes?

3 A box is weighed as shown opposite.

The contents are then divided into 4 equal parts.

How many grams does one part weigh?

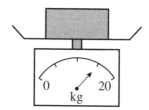

4 A cyclist travels 7 km in 20 minutes. Work out the cyclist's average speed in km/h

5 A motorbike travels at 20 m/s. A car travels at 70 km/h. Which vehicle is travelling faster?

6 Maya's watch is 8 minutes slow. Rahul's watch is 11 minutes fast.

Maya's arranges to meet Rahul at 14:45 by her watch. What time must Rahul use on his watch to make sure he is on time for meeting Maya?

7 Match speeds A and B opposite to their equivalent speeds in km/h as shown.

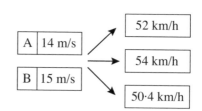

8 A car travels at a steady speed of 40 mph. How far does the car travel in 12 minutes?

9 Nick drinks 2000 ml of water during one day. Katzia says that this is far too much water. Do you agree with her or not? Give reasons for your answer.

10 Chang travels 8 miles in 10 minutes then a further $12\frac{1}{2}$ miles in the next 20 minutes.

Work out Chang's average speed for this combined journey.

TASK M9.2 ──────────────────────────────── **Main Book Page 233**

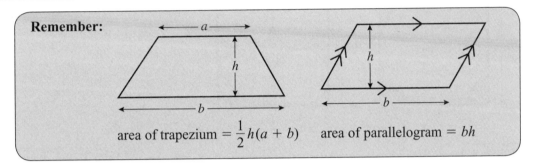

Remember:

area of trapezium $= \frac{1}{2}h(a + b)$ area of parallelogram $= bh$

Give answers to 1 decimal place when necessary.

1 Work out the area of each shape.

a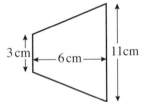

b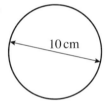

c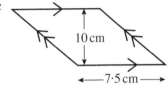

2 A semi-circular table top is shown opposite.
Work out its area in cm²

3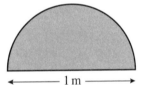

The area of the circle is 60 cm².
The ratio of the areas of the parallelogram to the circle is 3 : 5.
Work out the value of x.

4 A groundsman uses a paint spray with a wheel to paint the line for one side of a football pitch.
The wheel has diameter 30 cm. The wheel turns completely 84 times. How long is this side of the football pitch? Give the answer in metres.

5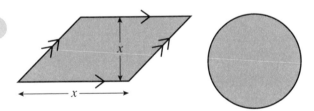

The area enclosed by the running track opposite is to be replaced with new turf.
The turf is bought in 20 m² loads which each cost £38.
How much will it cost to turf this entire area?

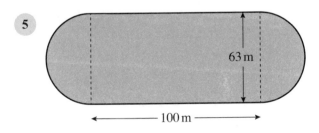

6

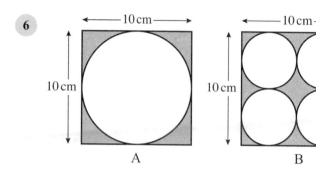

A

B

Which shaded area opposite is greater and by how much?

TASK M9.3 ——————————————————————— **Main Book Page 235**

> **Remember:** volume of prism = (Area of cross section) × length
> $$V = Al$$

Give answers to 1 decimal place when necessary.

Find the volume of each prism.

1

2

3

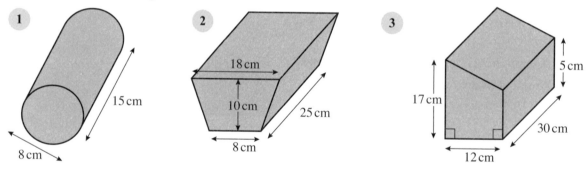

4

The volume of the triangular prism opposite is 320 cm³.

Work out the length x in the triangular cross-section as shown.

5 A cylindrical bucket has a diameter of 30 cm and a height of 35 cm.

How many full bucket loads of water are needed to fill up the tank opposite?

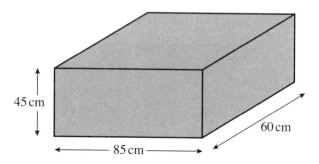

6

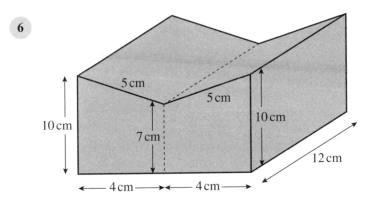

The prism opposite is varnished all over its surface area. It is given 2 coats of varnish.

The varnish costs £1·12 for each 100 cm².

Work out the total cost of the varnish used

7

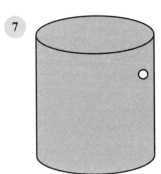

A barrel has a 25 cm diameter. The barrel is empty then water is poured in at a rate of 0·05 litres per second.

There is a hole in the barrel. The water enters the barrel for 5 minutes 14 seconds before it starts leaking through the hole.

Calculate the height of the hole above the base of the barrel.
(1 litre = 1000 cm³)

TASK M9.4 _____ | **Main Book Page 237** |

1 The length of a book is 23·4 cm, measured to the nearest 0·1 cm.

Write down   **a** the lower bound   **b** the upper bound

2 The width of a room is 3·8 m, measured to the nearest 0·1 m.

Write down   **a** the lower bound   **b** the upper bound

3 A woman weighs 63 kg correct to the nearest kg. What is her least possible weight?

4 Copy and complete the table.

A length l is 47·2 cm, to the nearest 0·1 cm, so		$\leqslant l <$	47·25
A mass m is 83 kg, to the nearest kg, so		$\leqslant m <$	
A Volume V is 7·3 m³, to the nearest 0·1 m³, so		$\leqslant V <$	
A radius r is 6·87 cm, to the nearest 0·01 cm, so		$\leqslant r <$	
An area A is 470 m², to the nearest 10 m², so		$\leqslant A <$	

5 The base and height of a triangle are measured to the nearest 0·1 cm.

    a Write down the upper bound for the base 3·4 cm.

    b Write down the lower bound for the height 4·8 cm.

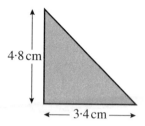

4·8 cm

3·4 cm

6 The capacity c of a jug is 503·4 ml, by measuring to the nearest 0·1 ml. Write down the upper and lower bounds as an inequality.

7 In a 200 m race a runner is timed at 23·46 seconds to the nearest 0·01 second. Write down the upper and lower bounds as an inequality.

8 The town of Hatton has a population of 8400, correct to the nearest 100. Tom says that the population may be as high as 8450. Explain clearly whether he is correct or not.

9

0·0017 cm   0·0018 cm   0·0019 cm

The width of a human hair is measured as 0·0018 cm to the nearest 0·0001 cm.

Write down the upper and lower bounds for this width as an inequality.

10 A company makes £1 million profit, correct to the nearest £100 000. What is the least amount of profit the company may have made.

TASK M9.5   **Main Book Page 239**

1 Truncate the numbers below to 2 decimal places.

    a 10·6184   **b** 29·321   **c** 7·68312

2 Write down an inequality for the possible values of each x below if x is truncated to 3 decimal places.

    a 4·236   **b** 715·187   **c** 26·548

3 The length, width and height of the cuboid are measured to the nearest cm.

volume = length × width × height

What is the lowest possible value of the volume of the cuboid?

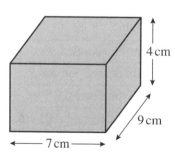

4 cm

9 cm

7 cm

4 Write down an inequality for the possible values of m if $m = 8.2$ when truncated to 1 decimal place.

5 The base and height of this triangle are measured to the nearest 0.1 m.

Calculate the lower and upper bounds for the area of this triangle.

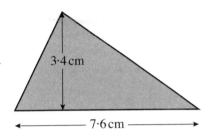

3.4 cm

7.6 cm

6 Amelia weighs 64 kg, truncated to the nearest kg. John weighs 64 kg, rounded off to the nearest kg. They sit opposite sides of a seesaw. If each person's weight is their lowest possible, who will sink to the ground? Explain your answer fully.

7 $n = 4700$ has been truncated to the nearest 100. Write down an inequality for the possible values of n.

8 Write down an inequality for the upper and lower bounds for each number below:

$d = 360$, correct to the nearest 20
$m = 45$, correct to the nearest 5
$x = 6.4$, correct to the nearest 0.2

9 The circumference of a tin is 25 cm, correct to the nearest mm. Identical tins are placed on the shelf shown opposite. What is the least number of tins which should fit on the shelf?

Explain your answer fully.

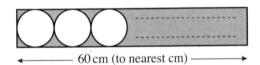

60 cm (to nearest cm)

TASK M9.6 ──────────────────────────── **Main Book Page 242**

Use  and if necessary in the questions below.

1 A solid weighs 450 g and has a volume of 50 cm³. Find the density of this solid.

2 A liquid has a density of 2 g/cm³. How much does the liquid weigh if its volume is 240 cm³

3 A metal bar has a density of 12 g/cm³ and a mass of 360 g. Find the volume of the metal bar.

4 A force of 42 N acts over an area of 8 m². Find the pressure.

5 A box weighs 160 N and exerts a pressure of 50 Pa on the floor. What is the area of the base of the box?

6 Which has a greater volume − 102·6 g of lead with density 11·4 g/cm³ or 78·85 g of steel with density 8·3 g/cm³? Write down by how much.

7 The density of this metal bar is 7·4 g/cm³.
Find the mass of this metal bar. Give your answer in kg.
(Note the length is given in metres.)

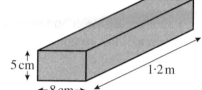

8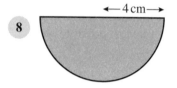

The base of a table leg is a semi-circle. A force acts through the leg creating a pressure of 8000 Pa. Work out the value of this force in Newtons.

9 A metal cube of length 0·2 m has a density of 8.3 g/cm³. A hole is bored through the cube with 485 cm³ of metal being removed. What is the mass in kg of the remaining piece of metal?

10 A cuboid has a mass of 6 kg which provides a weight of 60 N. The dimensions are 50 cm by 30 cm by 20 cm. On which face would the cuboid be standing if the greatest possible pressure were to be exerted on the ground? Explain your answer fully.

TASK E9.1 ——————————————————— **Main Book Page 244**

1 A car travels at x m/s. Write down an expression for this speed in km/hr.

2 A force of q Newtons provides a pressure across a square area.
Each side of the square is x cm long.
Write down an expression for the pressure in Pascals (Pa).

3 A train travels 253 km at an average speed of 92 km/hr then 45 km at an average speed of 10 m/s. Find the average speed for the whole journey in km/hr.

4 A metal bar has 3 holes cut completely through its length. The cross-sectional area of each hole is y cm². The density of the metal is 9 g/cm³.
Find the mass of the remaining piece of metal, giving your answer in terms of x and y.

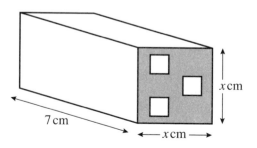

5 A cyclist travels at $3y$ km/hr. A car travels at $5x$ km/hr. Find an expression for the difference in the speeds of the car and cyclist in m/s.

6 Arlene travels for 48 minutes at 75 km/hr then for 1 hour 12 minutes at x km/hr. If she travels a total distance of 126 km, find the value of x.

7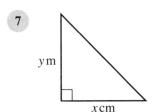

A force is applied over a triangular area as shown opposite. It provides a pressure of m Pa. Write down an expression for the force in Newtons.

8 Metal A has density x g/cm³ and metal B has density y g/cm³. m kg of metal A is mixed with n g of metal B to make an alloy.

Find an expression in terms of m, n, x and y for the density of this alloy.

TASK M9.7 ──────────────────────────────────── **Main Book Page 246**

In this exercise, O is always the centre of the circle. Give answers to one decimal place.

1 Find the length of arc AB.

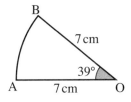

2 Find the length of arc AB.

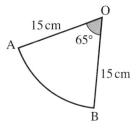

In questions **3** to **5**, find the perimeter of each shape, leaving answers in terms of π.

3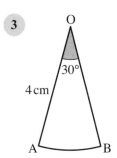

4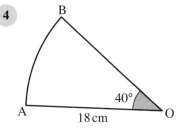

5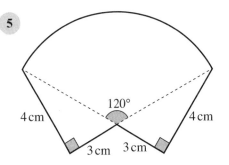

6 Pete calculates the arc length AB to be 8π cm.
Abigail says he is not correct.
Which person do you believe?
Explain your answer fully.

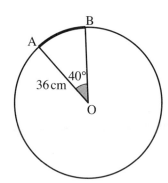

7 The arc PQ = 9 cm.
Find ∠PÔQ.

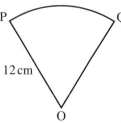

8 Use a calculator to find the perimeter of
the shaded area.

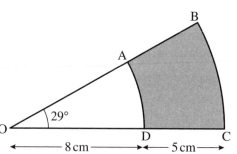

9 Use a calculator to find the perimeter of the
shaded area.

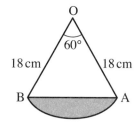

10 Calculate the perimeter of the shape ABCDE.

TASK M9.8 ———————————————————————— **Main Book Page 248**

In this exercise, O is always the centre of the circle. Give answers to one decimal place.

In questions (1) to (3), find each shaded area.

(1)
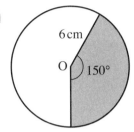

(2)
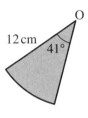

(3)
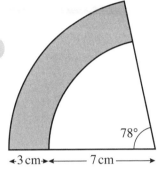

(4) Show that the area of this sector is exactly $\dfrac{16\pi}{9}$ cm².

(5) ODC is a sector of radius 4 cm.
Find the shaded area, leaving you answer in terms of π.
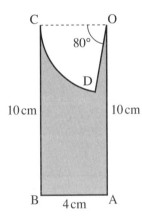

(6) Find the value of θ if the area of the sector is 90 cm².
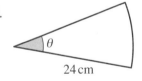

(7) Find the area of the shaded segment.
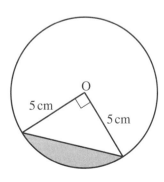

102

8

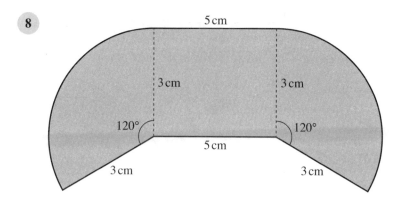

Prove that the 'exact' area of the shape opposite is $(6\pi + 15)\,\text{cm}^2$.

9

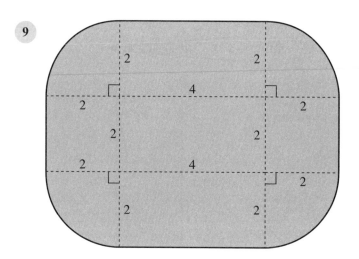

Calculate the total area of the shape opposite. All lengths are in cm.

TASK M9.9 ———————————————————— **Main Book Page 250**

> **Remember:** $1\,\text{m}^3 = 1000\,l = 1\,000\,000\,\text{cm}^3$
> $1\,\text{m}^2 = 10\,000\,\text{cm}^2$
> $1\,\text{litre} = 1000\,\text{cm}^3$

Give answers to 1 decimal place when necessary.

1

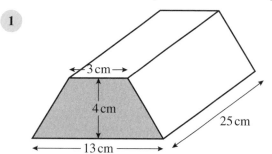

a Work out the volume of this prism in cm^3.

b What is the volume of this prism in m^3?

2 Which is the greater amount? $7 \cdot 2 \, \text{m}^3$ or $7 \, 090 \, 000 \, \text{cm}^3$

3 True or false? $6 \cdot 3 \, \text{m}^2 = 630 \, \text{cm}^2$

4 A rectangular tank has a length of 8 m and a width of 6 m. How high is the tank if it can hold 240 000 litres of water when full?

5 Copy and complete

a $4 \, \text{m}^3 = \boxed{} \, \text{cm}^3$

b $2 \cdot 9 \, \text{m}^3 = \boxed{} \, \text{cm}^3$

c $8 \, \text{m}^2 = \boxed{} \, \text{cm}^2$

d $7 \cdot 48 \, \text{m}^2 = \boxed{} \, \text{cm}^2$

e $6 \, 000 \, 000 \, \text{cm}^3 = \boxed{} \, \text{m}^3$

f $6 \, \text{m}^3 = \boxed{} \, \text{litres}$

g $6 \, 000 \, 000 \, \text{cm}^2 = \boxed{} \, \text{m}^2$

h $5 \cdot 16 \, \text{m}^3 = \boxed{} \, \text{litres}$

i $38 \, 000 \, \text{cm}^2 = \boxed{} \, \text{m}^2$

6 A pipe of diameter 8 cm and length 3 m is half full of water. How many litres of water are in the pipe?

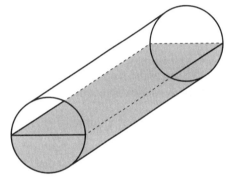

7

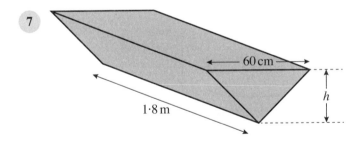

The trough opposite is full of water.

It contains 378 litres of water.

Calculate the height h of the trough.

8 The cylinder opposite is made with metal of density 9 g/cm³.

Prove that the mass of the prism is 'exactly' 3024π grams.

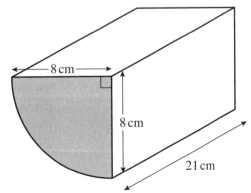

TASK M9.10 ━━━ **Main Book Page 252**

> **Remember:**   sphere   pyramid   cone
>
> volume $= \frac{4}{3}\pi^3$ volume $= \frac{1}{3} \times$ (base area) $\times h$ volume $= \frac{1}{3}\pi r^2 h$

In this exercise give answers to 3 significant figures where necessary.

1   Find the volume of each solid.

a

14 cm

23 cm

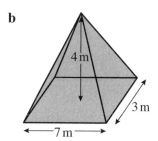

b

4 m

3 m

7 m

c

2·5 m

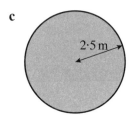

2   A hemisphere and a cone are both made from the same material. The cone has a base diameter of 8 cm and a perpendicular height of 6 cm. The hemisphere has a diameter of 7 cm. Which solid weighs more?

3   Find the 'exact' volume of each solid, leaving your answers in terms of π.

a

4 cm

3 cm

16 cm

15 cm

b

9 cm

25 cm

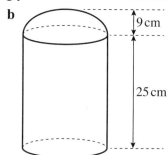

(hemisphere on a cylinder)

4   A bowl is in the shape of a hemisphere with diameter 18 cm.
Water is poured into the bowl at a rate of 12 cm³/s.
How long will it take to fill the bowl completely?
Give the answer to the nearest second.

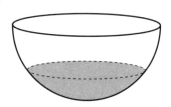

5

12 cm

20 cm

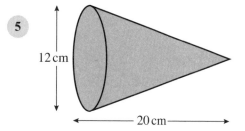

The cone opposite is made from a metal with density 9 g/cm³.

Find the 'exact' mass of the cone, leaving the answer in terms of π.

6 A pyramid has a square base of side length 8 cm and a perpendicular height of 17 cm. The pyramid has the same volume as a cone of base radius 6·5 cm. Find the perpendicular height of the cone.

7 A sphere has a volume of 80 cm³. Find the radius of the sphere.

TASK M9.11 ———————————————————— **Main Book Page 255**

> **Remember:**   sphere   cylinder   cone
>
> surface area = $4\pi r^2$ curved surface area = $2\pi rh$ curved surface area = πrl
> where l is the slant height

In this exercise give answers to 3 significant figures where necessary.

1 Find the *curved* surface area of each solid.

a   **b**   **c**

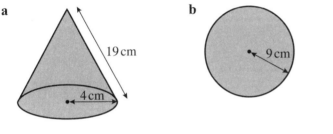

2 Find the *total* surface area of this cone, leaving your answer in terms of π.

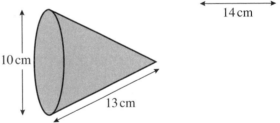

3

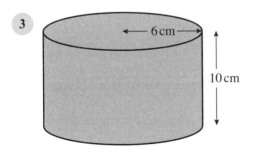

Prove that the *total* surface area of the cylinder opposite is 192π cm².

4 A cone is attached to a cylinder of diameter 12 cm as shown. The perpendicular height of the cylinder is equal to its diameter. Find the *total* surface area of the combined solid.

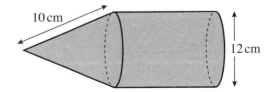

5 A cone has curved surface area 30 cm² and slant height 4 cm. Calculate the radius of the base of the cone.

6 The curved surface area of a hemisphere is $72\,\pi$ cm².
   a Find the radius of the hemisphere.
   b Work out the 'exact' total surface area of the hemisphere.

7

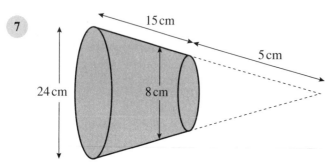

Calculate the total surface area of the frustum opposite.

8 A sphere has a surface area of 480 cm². Calculate its diameter.

9 Use Pythagoras to find the slant height of the cone opposite then calculate the total surface area of the cone.

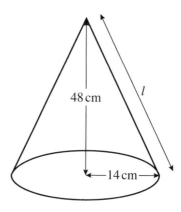

| TASK M9.12 | Main Book Page 258 |

1

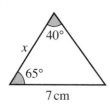
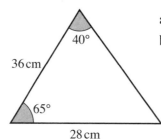

a Explain why these triangles are similar.
b Work out the value of x.

2 Rectangles A and B are similar. Find x.

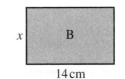

3 Shapes C and D are similar. Find y and z.

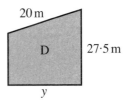

4 **a** Prove that triangles QRS and PRT are similar.
   b Work out the value of x.

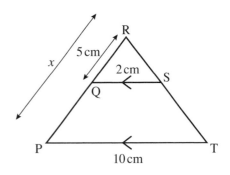

5 **a** Prove that triangles ABE and ACD
      are similar.
   b Work out the value of y.

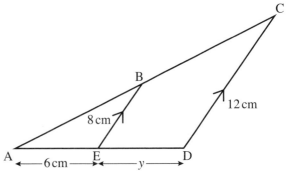

6 Use similar triangles to find x in each diagram below.

   a

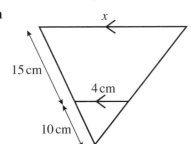

   b

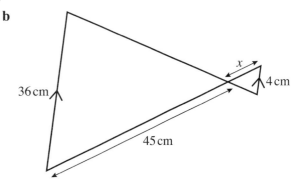

108

 Main Book Page 259

In questions **1** to **3**, find *x*.

1
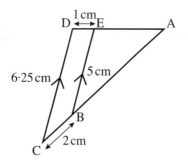

2
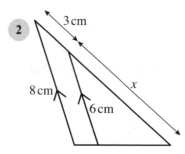

3
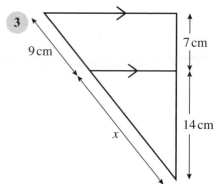

4 Find AB and AE.
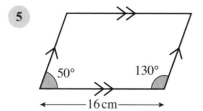

5
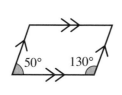

a Explain why these two parallelograms are similar.

b The perimeter of the larger parallelogram is 48 cm. The perimeter of the smaller parallelogram is 30 cm. Work out the length of the smaller side of the smaller parallelogram.

6 a Explain why triangles PQR and STR are similar.
b Find the length of ST.
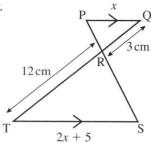

7 Find x and y.

17·5 cm

x

31·5 cm

y

4 cm

14 cm

8 Find x.

$3y$

$4x - 2$

$x + 1$

y

9 Find x and y.

$5\frac{1}{3}$ cm

x

25 cm

y

6 cm   4 cm

10

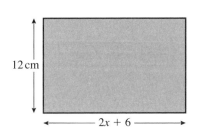

8 cm

$x + 6$

12 cm

$2x + 6$

The two rectangles are mathematically similar.

Work out the area of the larger rectangle

STATISTICS 2   10

TASK M10.1 ———————————————— **Main Book Page 269**

Give answers to one decimal place when appropriate.

1 When they last recycled something, 600 children were asked if they recycled paper, bottles or cans. The information is shown in the two-way table below.

	Paper	Bottle	Cans	Total
Boys		73	89	
Girls				352
Total	306	131		600

  a Copy and complete the two-way table.

  b How many girls recycled paper last time they recycled something?

  c What percentage of the children recycled cans?

2 The mean average age of 9 people is 42. What is the total of all their ages?

3 Some people were asked what their favourite type of fruit is. The information is recorded in the table below.

Type of fruit	Frequency (number of people)
apple	28
orange	17
pear	8
banana	33
other	4

Draw a pie chart to display this information.

4 Charlotte sells cars. Her number of sales is shown in the pictogram below.

April	
May	
June	
July	
August	

means 8 cars

a She sells 14 cars in June. Copy and complete the pictogram.

b She is paid an extra £250 for each car she sells. How much extra is she paid for the months in the pictogram.

c If during July she was paid an additional 5% per car sale, how much would she have been paid for July only?

5 The mean amount of weekly pocket money for 36 boys is £4·50.

The mean amount of weekly pocket money for 14 girls is £5·50.

Find the mean amount of weekly pocket money for all 50 children.

6 **a** Draw an ordered stem and leaf diagram for lengths of worms (in cm) shown below for a Science experiment.

Stem	Leaf
10	
11	
12	
13	

12·3	11·7	12·2	10·9	11·6	10·9
11·6	10·7	12·4	13·3	12·2	11·7
12·4	11·5	11·9	10·7	12·2	10·9

b Work out the difference between the median and 12.2 cm.

7

The range of the 5 numbers above is equal to the median 12. The mode is 14.

Write down all 5 numbers if the mean average is equal to 10.

1. The vertical line graph opposite shows the ages of the players for Grafton Town Rugby Team.

   The stem and leaf diagram below shows the ages of the players for the Colby Rugby Team.

   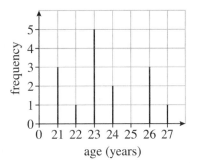

Stem	Leaf
1	8 9
2	1 2 5 7 7 8 8 8
3	0 1 1 3 4

   Compare the ages of the players in each team.
   (Remember to mention the average and the spread of data.)

2. 100 people are surveyed about their weekly pay. 50 people from Banford have mean average pay £460. 30 people in Darrington have mean average pay of £340. 20 people from Dalton have mean average pay equal to the mean average pay of all 100 people. Find the mean average pay of all 100 people.

3. The pie charts below show the favourite subjects of students from Hatton High School and Wilton Green School.

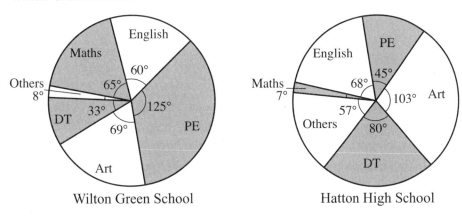

Wilton Green School   Hatton High School

Arjun says that 'more students like PE in Wilton Green School then Hatton High School'.
Do you agree with Arjun? Explain your answer clearly.

4. 1000 people in Birmingham and Nottingham travel to work by car, by walking, by bike or by train. 314 out of the 530 people who travel by car live in Birmingham. 69 people from Birmingham travel by train. 117 people from Birmingham walk and 175 people from Nottingham walk. 41 out of 72 people who travel by bike come from Nottingham.

   a One of the people from Birmingham *only* is chosen. What is the probability that this person travels to work by bike?

   b What percentage of the people asked travel to work by train?

5 Some students go on a school skiing holiday. The table below shows which year group they belong to.

Year group	Frequency
7	6
8	10
9	16
10	24
11	16

Draw a pie chart to display this information.

6 Some young people are asked how much they earn each week for their part time jobs. The information is shown in the stem and diagram.

Stem	Leaf
2	4 5 5 8
3	0 0 0 5 7 8
4	0 4 4 5 5 5 5
5	0 4

$3|7 = £37$

Group this data into the intervals $20 - 29$, $30 - 39$, $40 - 49$ and $50 - 59$ then draw a frequency diagram.

Example:

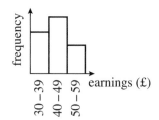

7 **a** 6, 7, 8, 9 and 10 are five consecutive integers. Work out the mean average of the squares of these five integers.

b $(n - 2)$, $(n - 1)$, n, $(n + 1)$, $(n + 2)$ are five consecutive integers.

Find and simplify an expression for the mean average of the squares of these five integers.

TASK M10.3 ———————————————— **Main Book Page 275**

1 The table below shows the number of times various people have been swimming during one month.

Number of swims	0	1	2	3	4	5	6
Frequency	7	5	10	9	11	5	3

a Write down the modal number of swims.

b Find the median number of swims.

c Work out the mean average number of swims.

2 Some teenagers in 2 areas of a city were asked how many pairs of shoes they owned.
The results shown in the tables below.

Area A

Number of pairs of shoes	1	2	3	4	5	6
Frequency	5	11	28	24	8	3

Area B

Number of pairs of shoes	1	2	3	4	5	6
Frequency		1	6	23	61	42	24

a Work out the mean number of pairs of shoes for each area, giving your answer to one decimal place.

b In which area do your results suggest that teenagers own more pairs of shoes per person?

3 Some students in Year 11 sit a memory test, marked out of 10. The results for students in class 11B are shown in the table below.

Mark	Frequency
4	2
5	6
6	4
7	8
8	7
9	3
10	1

The students in class 11A have a median score of 5 and a range of 9. Compare the test scores for the two classes.

4 The table below shows the weights of some newborn babies.

Weight w (kg)	$2 < w \leqslant 2.5$	$2.5 < w \leqslant 3$	$3 < w \leqslant 3.5$	$3.5 < w \leqslant 4$	$4 < w \leqslant 4.5$
Frequency	8	36	83	54	19

a Estimate the total weight of all the babies.

b Estimate the mean average weight of all the babies.

5 The salaries for the workers in a small company are shown below.

Salary s (£1000s)	$10 < s \leqslant 18$	$18 < s \leqslant 26$	$26 < s \leqslant 34$	$34 < s \leqslant 42$
Frequency	3	14	11	5

Maggie says that 'the modal interval also contains the median'. Explain clearly whether she is correct or not.

6 Some people were asked how many portions of vegetable they ate last Sunday. The amounts are shown in the table below.

Number of portions	0	1	2	3	4	5	6
Frequency		5	14	n	23	n	9	5

An equal number of people said they had 2 portions as had 4 portions.
The mean average number of portions was 2.875.
How many people said they had 2 portions of vegetables?

TASK M10.4 ──────────────────────────── **Main Book Page 278**

1 A local post office sells cards. The table below shows how many cards were sold during a one-year period.

Month	Jan	Feb	Mar	Apr	May	Jun	Jul	Aug	Sep	Oct	Nov	Dec
Number of cards	60	440	80	380	100	40	60	20	300	460	580	560

a Draw a line graph for the information in this table.

b Find the mean average for the first 4 months: Jan, Feb, Mar, Apr.
Pilot this average on the graph at the midpoint of the 4 months.

c Keep moving along one month and finding the 4-point moving average (i.e. use a group of 4 months). Plot the new moving average on the graph each time.

d Join up the moving average points with a dotted line. Comment on the trend of card sales during this year. Write down any reasons for this trend.

2 The table below shows how many houses have been sold by an estate agent during a 15-year period.

Year	2001	2002	2003	2004	2005	2006	2007	2008	2009	2010	2011	2012	2013	2014	2015
Number of houses sold	135	45	135	150	30	180	165	60	180	135	165	195	45	180	150

a Draw a line graph for the information in this table.

b Find the 3-point moving average. (i.e. use groups of 3 years). Plot the new moving average on the graph each time.

c Join up the moving average points with a dotted line. Comment on the trend of house sales during these 15 years.

3 The table below shows how many people visit a local castle each day during a 3-week period.

	Mon	Tue	Wed	Thu	Fri	Sat	Sun
Week 1	90	75	100	115	140	210	180
Week 2	55	75	114	115	147	224	187
Week 3	62	68	107	129	182	210	201

a Draw a line graph for the information in this table.

b Find the 7-point moving average.

c Plot the moving average points on the graph and join them up with a dotted line.

d Comment on the trend shown.

1   Write down what X and Y might be to give this scatter graph.

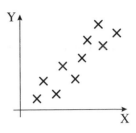

2   The table below shows the heights and neck lengths of 15 people.

Height (cm)	177	187	195	162	200	175	192	186	200	165	200	172	198	181	190
Neck length (cm)	6·9	7·5	7·5	5·5	8·5	6·1	6·8	6·8	13	6	8	5·7	7·7	6·9	7·8

a   Copy and complete this scatter graph to show the data in the table.

b   Draw the line best fit.

c   One of the points does not follow the trend. Write down the values of this point.

d   Describe the correlation for the points that follow the trend.

e   A person is 184 cm tall. Use your line of best fit to find out the person's likely neck length.

f   Another person has a neck length of 7.7 cm. How tall is the person likely to be?

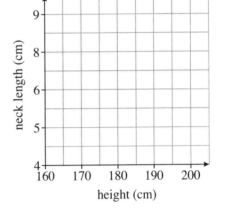

3   This scatter graph shows information about cars. Write down what you think Y might be.

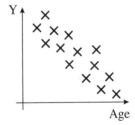

4   A golfer records his weekly average score and how many hours he practises each week (in golf a score of 70 is *better* than a score of 80!)

The information is shown in the table below.

Weekly average score	79	75	87	81	84	73	77	88	72	78	84	76
Weekly hours practising	22	24	19	21	22	23	24	17	26	22	19	21

a Draw a scatter graph to show the data at the bottom of the last page. Use the *x*-axis for the weekly average score from 70 to 90. Use the *y*-axis for the weekly hours practising from 0 to 30.

b Describe the correlation in this scatter graph.

c Draw the line of best fit.

d If the golfer practised for 25 hours one week, what average score would you expect the golfer to get that week?

e An average weekly score of under 60 in golf would be impossible. Explain why the line of best fit cannot be used to work out the average score for a golfer if the golfer practises for 45 hours one week.

TASK M10.6 ────────────────────────────── **Main Book Page 284**

1 Write down which samples below are likely to be representative.
For any sample which is not representative give a reason why it is not.

a To find out the average number of cars owned by each family in a particular city.
The sample is chosen by randomly selecting 10% of the streets in the city and visiting each house to establish the number of cars.

b To find out who people will vote for at the next Local Election in a certain town.
The sample is chosen by asking people as they enter the town's largest supermarket.

c To find out the percentage of the crowd entering a football ground who are female.
The sample is chosen by recording the sex of every 10th person as they pass through the gates.

d To find out the average amount of time people spend exercising each week.
The sample is chosen by asking people as they enter a local gym.

e To find out the average number of computers per household.
The sample is chosen by selecting at random people from 10% of the addresses from the electoral register.

f To find out the number of the birds which visit gardens in the UK.
The sample is chosen by selecting every 20th name from every telephone directory in the UK and asking each of these people to record the number of birds.

2 Describe how you would select a representative sample for each of the following:

a To find out the most popular rock bands of people under 18 years old.

b To find out the most popular holiday destinations of people in Scotland.

c To survey pupils in a school about how they get to and from school each day.

d To investigate the most popular drinks of people in a certain city.

TASK M10.7 ———————————————————— **Main Book Page 287**

1 625 people go to the theatre to watch a famous comedian. 392 of these people are male.
A stratified sample of 50 people is to be taken from the males and females in the audience to
find out their opinions on the concert. How many males and how many females will be chosen?

2 900 people return from their holidays. 284 people went skiing, 109 visited Australasia,
321 took city breaks in Europe and the rest had visited the Caribbean.

A holiday company wishes to find out about the quality of service in the hotels these people
stayed in. They decide to take a stratified sample of 70 people. What should be the sample size
for each of the holiday destinations: skiing, Australasia, European cities and the Caribbean?

3 Rachel needs to survey opinions from people visiting the local swimming pool. Explain how
Rachel could take a simple random sample.

4 The table below shows the number of people who voted for each party at a general Election in
one constituency.

Party	Number of votes
Labour	16 201
Conservative	12 374
Liberal Democrat	9 812
Green	7 104
Others	387

It is wanted to take a stratified sample of 2000 people to find out more about their opinions on
major issues.

How many people from each chosen party would be selected in the stratified sample?

5 A 5% stratified sample of 40 people is taken from a group according to whether they can drive
or not. The number of people in the sample is shown below.

	Drive	Not drive	Total
Male	18	5	23
Female	13	4	17
Total	31	9	40

What is the lowest possible number of males who do not drive in the whole group of people?

6 In a certain school, a choice from 3 languages is offered in Year 7.

The take-up is shown below.

Language	Number of pupils
French	139
German	69
Spanish	42

A sample of 25 pupils is to be taken to question them about their attitudes to languages.

a Explain why you would want to use a stratified sample.

b Work out how many pupils you would want in your sample from each language.

GEOMETRY 3   11

TASK M11.1 ———————————————————— **Main Book Page 295**

1 Use a ruler and compasses only to draw:

a
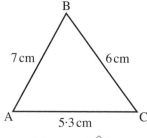
Measure AĈB

b
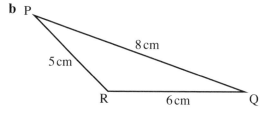
Measure PR̂Q

2 Use a ruler and protractor to draw:

a
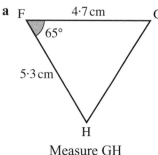
Measure GH

b
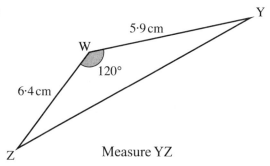
Measure YZ

3 A map has scale 1:400000. On the map Henby is 3 cm from Dexford and Henby is 4·9 cm from Cowley. What is the real extra distance of Henby from Cowley compared to Henby from Dexford?

4 Use a ruler and compasses only to construct an equilateral triangle with side length 7 cm.

5 **a** Make an accurate scale drawing of the trapezium opposite, using a scale of 1 cm for every 3 m.

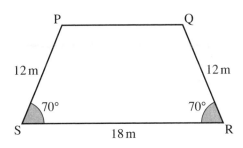

b Measure then write down the real length of PQ.

c Work out the area of the trapezium.
Remember: area of trapezium $= \frac{1}{2} h(a + b)$.

6 Harold needs to draw an 810 m stretch of road on a map. The scale of the map is 1:30000. How long will the stretch of road be on the map?

7 Draw a triangle ABC such that AC = 6·5 cm, BÂC = 48° and AĈB = 63°.
Measure the length of AB.

TASK M11.2	**Main Book Page 296**

1

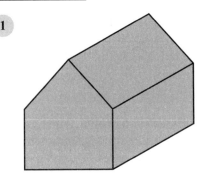

Write down the sum of the number of faces and the number of vertices for the prism shown opposite.

2 Gideon leaves his tent and walks on a bearing of 330° for 5 km.
He then walks due East for 8 km.

a Use a scale of 1 cm for 1 km to draw this journey.

b How far is he now from his tent?

c On what bearing must Gideon now walk if he wants to walk directly back to his tent?

North

•
tent

3 The plan and elevations of a cuboid are shown below. Each square has area 1 cm². Work out the total surface of the cuboid.

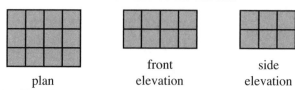

plan   front elevation   side elevation

4

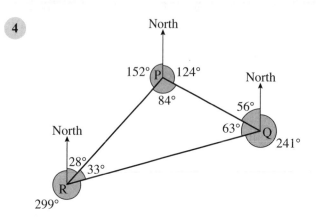

Alma travels from P to R then R to Q and finally from Q to P.

Work out the bearing she walked on from

a P to R

b R to Q

c Q to P

5 The longest diagonal of a kite ABCD is 6 units.

a Copy the diagram opposite and mark on the point D. Write down the co-ordinates of D.

b Write down the co-ordinates of the intersection of the diagonals of the kite.

c Work out the area of the kite ABCD.

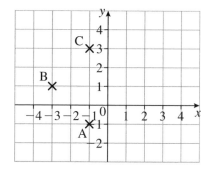

6

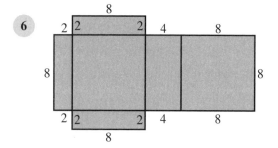

Liam has drawn this net for a cuboid. Anna says that this net will not work. Explain clearly why Anna believes this to be the case.

7

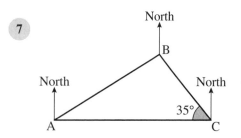

$\widehat{ABC}$ in the diagram opposite is treble the size of $\widehat{ACB}$. C is due East of A.

Work out the bearing of B from A.

8

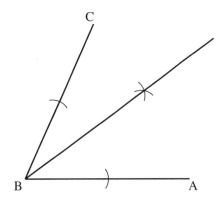

a Mark a point S on the diagram opposite to make a square PQRS.

b Write down the co-ordinates of the midpoint of QR.

c Mark on the point M at (0, 1). Mark on the point N so that the area of triangle QNM is exactly double the area of triangle QRM. Write down the co-ordinates of N.

TASK M11.3 ———————————————————— **Main Book Page 299**

1 Draw $\hat{ABC} = 70°$.
Construct the bisector of the angle.
Use a protractor to check each half of the angle now measures 35°.

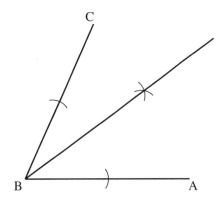

2 Draw any angle and construct the bisector of this angle.

3 Draw a horizontal line AB of length 7 cm.
Construct the perpendicular bisector of AB.
Check that each half of the line measures 3·5 cm exactly.

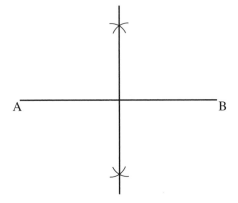

4 Draw any vertical line. Construct the perpendicular bisector of the line.

5   **a**   Draw PQ and QR at right angles to each other as shown.

      b   Construct the perpendicular bisector of QR.

      c   Construct the perpendicular bisector of PQ.

      d   The two perpendicular bisectors meet at a point
         (label this as S). Measure QS.

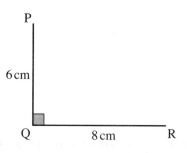

6   **a**   Draw $A\hat{B}C = 108°$ by using a protractor.

      b   Construct the bisector of this angle.

      c   Construct the bisector of one of the new angles.

      d   Check with a protractor that you have now drawn
         an angle of 27°.

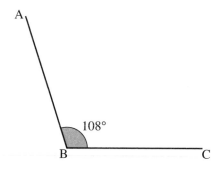

TASK E11.1   **Main Book Page 301**

1   Construct an equilateral triangle with each side equal to 8 cm.

2   Construct an angle of 60°.

3   **a**   Draw a line 8 cm long and mark the point A as shown.

              5 cm   A   3 cm

    b   Construct an angle of 90° at A.

4   **a**   Draw a line 10 cm long and mark the point B on the line as shown.

            4 cm   B   6 cm

    b   Construct an angle of 45° at B.

5   Construct a right-angled triangle ABC, where $A\hat{B}C = 90°$, BC = 6 cm and $A\hat{C}B = 60°$.
    Measure the length of AB.

6   Construct this triangle with ruler and compasses only.
    Measure x.

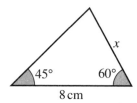

7 Draw any line and any point A.
Construct the perpendicular from the point A
to the line.

•A

_____

8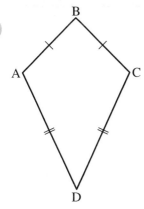

Construct the kite shown opposite with AC = 6 cm,
AB = BC = 5 cm and the whole kite area = 33 cm².
Measure the length AD.

9 **a** Construct this triangle with ruler and compasses only.
Measure QR.

b Explain clearly how you constructed the 30° angle.

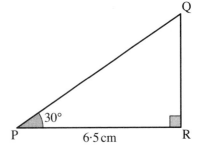

TASK M11.4 ——————————————————————— **Main Book Page 304**

You will need a ruler and a pair of compasses.

1 Draw the locus of all points which are less than or equal to 3 cm from a point A.

2 Draw the locus of all points which are exactly 4 cm from a point B.

3 Draw the locus of all points which are exactly 4 cm
from the line PQ.

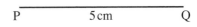

P   5 cm   Q

4 A triangular garden has a tree at the corner B.

The whole garden is made into a lawn except for anywhere
less than or equal to 6 m from the tree. Using a scale of
1 cm for 3 m, draw the garden and shade in the lawn.

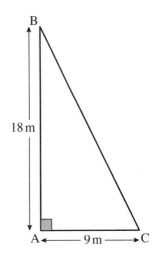

5 In a field a goat is attached by a rope to a peg P as shown. The rope is 30 m long. Using a scale of 1 cm for 10 m, copy the diagram then shade the area that the goat can roam in.

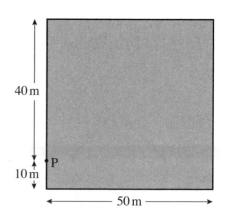

6 Draw the square opposite.

Draw the locus of all the points *outside* the square which are 3 cm from the edge of the square.

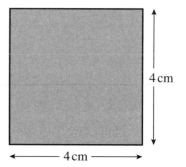

7 Each square is 1 m wide. The shaded area shows a building.

A guard dog is attached by a chain 5 m long to the point A on the outside of the building.

Draw the diagram on squared paper then shade the region the dog can cover.

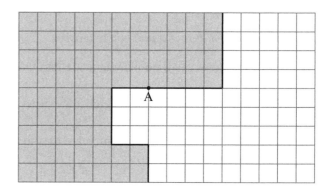

TASK M11.5 ———————————————— **Main Book Page 306**

You will need a ruler and a pair of compasses.

1 Construct the locus of points which are the same distance from the lines AB and BC (the bisector of angle B).

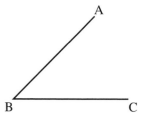

2 Faye wants to lay a path in her garden that is always the same distance from KL and KN.

Using a scale of 1 cm for 10 m, draw the garden and construct a line to show where the path will be laid.

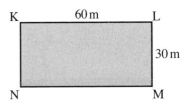

3 Construct the locus of points which are equidistant (the same distance) from M and N.

4 Draw A and B 7 cm apart.

A •   • B

A radar at A has a range of 150 km and a radar at B has a range of 90 km. Using a scale of 1 cm for every 30 km, show the area which can be covered by both radars at the same time.

5 Draw one copy of this diagram.

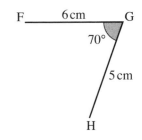

   a Construct the perpendicular bisector of FG and the bisector of FĜH.

   b Mark with a × the point which is equidistant from F and G as well as the same distance from the lines FG and GH.

6 Draw one copy of triangle PQR and show on it:

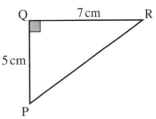

   a the perpendicular bisector of QR.

   b the bisector of PR̂Q.

   c the locus of points nearer to PR than to QR *and* nearer to R than to Q.

TASK M11.6   **Main Book Page 308**

1 Draw and label the plan and a side elevation for:

   a a cuboid.

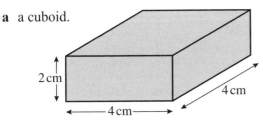

   b a cone.

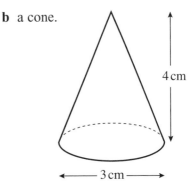

2 You are given the plan and two elevations of an object. Draw each object (on isometric paper if you wish to).

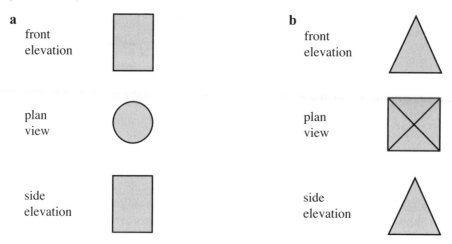

a
front
elevation

plan
view

side
elevation

b
front
elevation

plan
view

side
elevation

3 Draw a front elevation, plan view and side elevation of each solid below:

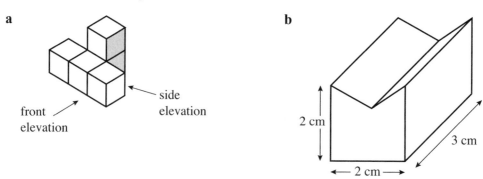

a
side
elevation
front
elevation

b
2 cm
3 cm
2 cm

4 Which solid below has the greater surface area and by how much if each square is 1 cm²?

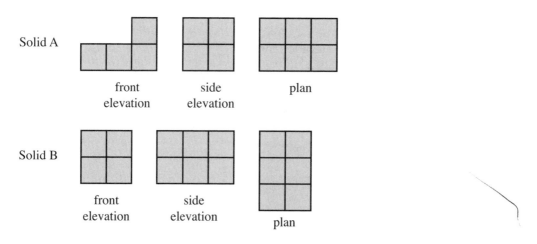

Solid A
front
elevation
side
elevation
plan

Solid B
front
elevation
side
elevation
plan

5 Two objects are made with 1 cm cubes. Their plans and elevations are shown below. How many cubes are used to make each solid?

a front
elevation

plan
view

side
elevation

b front
elevation

plan
view

side
elevation

6 Draw a plan, front elevation and side elevation of any cuboid with total surface area 42cm².

TASK M11.7 ———————————————————— **Main Book Page 311**

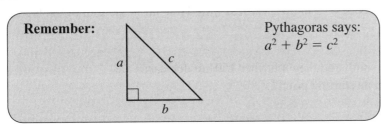

Remember:

Pythagoras says:
$a^2 + b^2 = c^2$

You will need a calculator. Give your answers correct to 2 decimal places where necessary.
The units are cm.

1 Find the length AB.

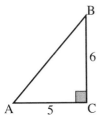

2 Find the length KL.

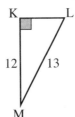

3 Find the length x.

a
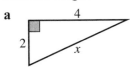

b
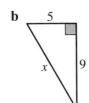

c
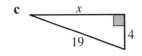

4 Find the length QR.

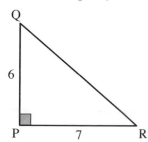

5 Find the length BC.

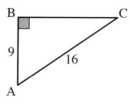

6 A rectangle has length 9 cm and width 7 cm. Calculate the length of its diagonal.

7 Calculate the perimeter of this triangle.

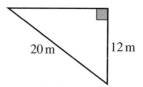

8 A ladder of length 7·5 m reaches 5·5 m up a vertical wall. How far is the foot of the ladder from the wall?

9 A plane flies 100 km due south and then a further 150 km due east. How far is the plane from its starting point?

10 Calculate the area of this triangle.

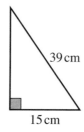

| **TASK E11.2** | **Main Book Page 313** |

You may use a calculator. Give answers to 2 decimal places.

1 Calculate the length AB in the diagram opposite.

2 Calculate the length of the line joining (1, 3) to (4, 7).

3 A triangle has vertices P(4 ,5), Q(6 ,9) and R(9, 1). Calculate the perimeter of the triangle PQR.

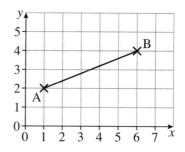

4 Find the height of each isosceles triangle below:

a

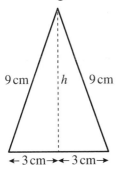

9 cm h 9 cm

←3 cm→←3 cm→

b

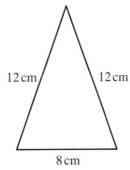

12 cm 12 cm

8 cm

5 Find the area of this isosceles triangle.

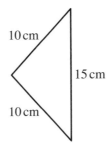

10 cm

15 cm

10 cm

6 Find the perimeter of this trapezium.

6 cm

13cm

10 cm

7

Remember: Volume of cone $= \frac{1}{3}\pi r^2 h$

curved surface area $= \pi r l$
where h = perpendicular height
and l = slant height

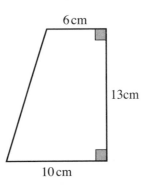

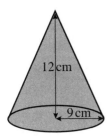

12 cm

9 cm

Work out the curved surface area of this cone.

8 Work out the volume of the cone opposite.

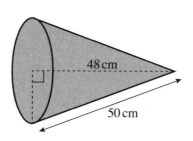

9 Find x.

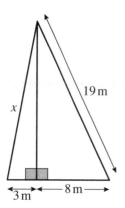

19 m

x

3 m ⟵ 8 m ⟶

10

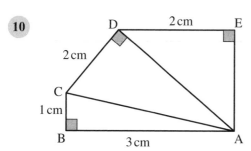

D   2 cm   E

2 cm

C

1 cm

B   3 cm   A

Calculate the length AE.

TASK M11.8 ──────────────────────────── **Main Book Page 316**

In each triangle below, note the angle given and state whether the identified side is in the correct position or not.

1

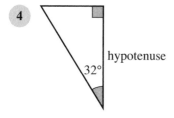

opposite

41°

2

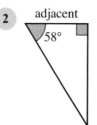

adjacent

58°

3

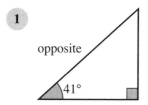

63°

adjacent

4

hypotenuse

32°

5

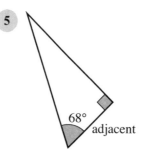

68° adjacent

6

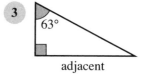

53°

opposite

7

8 opposite 82°

TASK M11.9 ──────── **Main Book Page 317**

For each triangle below, find the sides marked with letters, correct to 3 significant figures.

All lengths are in cm.

1 34, 18°, a

2 b, 23, 37°

3 c, 8·6, 43°

4 d, 39°, 14

5 17·3, 64°, e

6 15, 53°, f

7 g, 28°, 6·8

8 h, 74°, 7·9

9 Find the lengths of
a BD
b CD

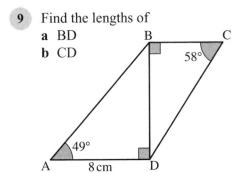

10 Find the length of PS.

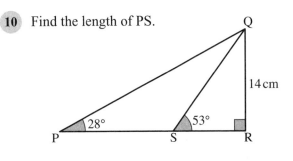

132

11 Find the length of KN.

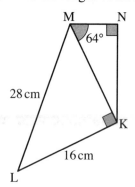

12 Find the length of TU.

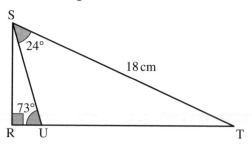

| **TASK M11.10** | **Main Book Page 319** |

For each triangle below, find the angles marked, correct to one decimal place.
All lengths are in cm.

1

15, 7, *a*

2

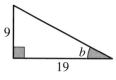

9, 19, *b*

3

5, *c*, 28

4

12·4, 6, *d*

5

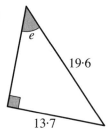

e, 19·6, 13·7

6

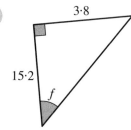

3·8, 15·2, *f*

7

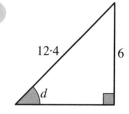

g, 46, 8·2

8

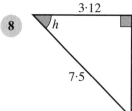

3·12, *h*, 7·5

9 Find the value of AB̂C.

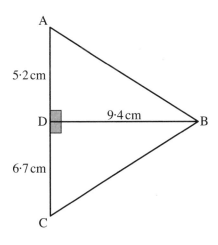

10 **a** Find the length QS.
b Find the value of RŜP.

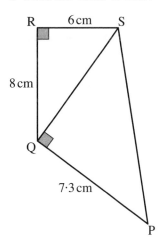

11 If PS : SR = 2 : 5, find the value of SQ̂R.

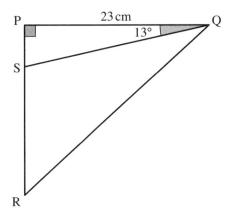

TASK E11.3 ────────────────────────── **Main Book Page 321**

1

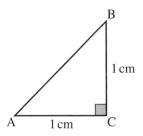

a Work out the value of BÂC.
b Work out the 'exact' length of AB, i.e. give the answer in the form $\sqrt{n}$ where n is an integer (whole number).
c Write down the 'exact' value of sin 45°.
d Write down the value of tan 45°.

2

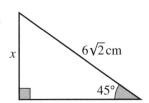

Find the 'exact' value of x.

3 **a** Work out the value of BÂC.

   b Write down the length AM.

   c Work out the 'exact' length of BM, i.e. give the answer in the form $\sqrt{n}$ where n is an integer (whole number).

   d Write down the 'exact' values of:

   a $\cos 60°$ **b** $\tan 60°$ **c** $\sin 60°$

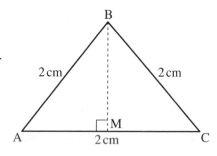

4

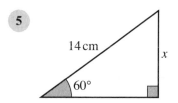

Find the 'exact' value of x.

5

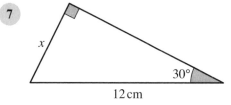

Find the 'exact' value of x, i.e. give the answer in the form $k\sqrt{3}$ where k is an integer.

6 By memory or looking in a book or researching, match the $\sin 30°$, $\cos 30°$ and $\tan 30°$ to the correct values shown opposite.

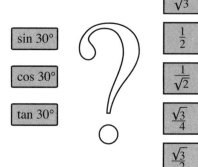

7

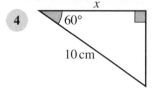

Find the value of x.

8 Find the 'exact' perimeter of each triangle, i.e. do not use a calculator and leave square roots in each answer.

   a

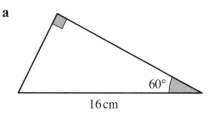

   b

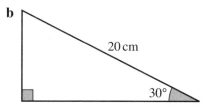

9 Without using a calculator, show that
$3 \tan 60° - 4 \cos 30° = \sqrt{3}$

9 Without using a calculator, find the value of AB̂C.

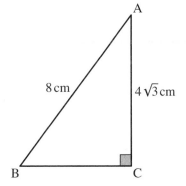

TASK M11.11 ────────────── **Main Book Page 322**

In this exercise give each answer to 3 significant figures or 1 decimal place.

1 Find AB̂C.

2 Find PR.

3 Find LM.

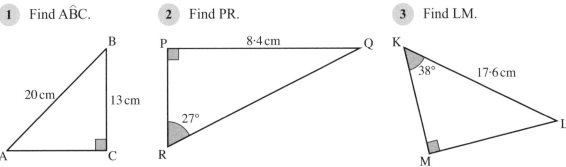

4 Find XZ.

5 Find AB̂C.

6 Find PQ.

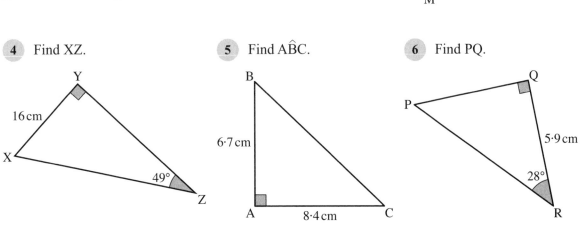

7 A ladder leans against a vertical wall so that it makes an angle of 29° with the wall. The top of the ladder reaches 3·4 m up the wall. How far is the base of the ladder from the wall?

8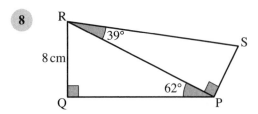

Calculate the length PS.

9 A builder wants a metal support to be inclined at an angle of 40° to the horizontal. If the vertical height from the bottom to the top of the support is 3·8 m, what is the length of the metal support?

10 Find the length of PQ.

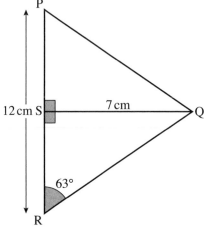

TASK E11.4 ——————————————————— **Main Book Page 324**

In this exercise give each answer to 3 significant figures or 1 decimal place.

1 AC = BC and MC = 7 cm.
Find the area of triangle ABC.

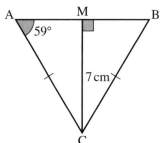

2 O is the centre of a circle of radius 6 cm.
If AÔB = 50°, find the area of
triangle AOB.

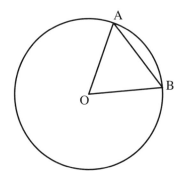

3 A field is 12 km due North of a village church. A balloon leaves the field and flies on a bearing of 138° until it lands due East of the village church. Calculate how far the balloon is now from the village church.

4 Find the value of AD̂B if BD = 18 cm.

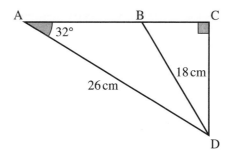

5 Work out the 'exact' perimeter of triangle ABC, without using a calculator.

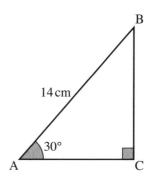

6

$$\sin P\hat{Q}R = \frac{7}{25} \quad \cos P\hat{Q}R = \frac{24}{25} \quad \tan P\hat{Q}R = \frac{7}{24}$$

Without using a calculator, work out

a the length RP.

b the area of triangle PQR.

7 PQRS is a kite.
Find the length of PS.

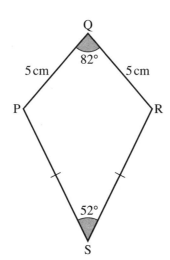

138

8 Find the length of AD.

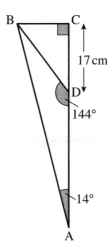